Exploring maths

5

Anita Straker, Tony Fisher, Rosalyn Hyde,
Sue Jennings and Jonathan Longstaffe

Published and distributed by Pearson Education Limited, Edinburgh Gate, Harlow, Essex, CM20 2JE, England
www.longman.co.uk

First published 2008

ISBN-13 978-1-405-84420-8

Freelance development editor: Sue Glover

Typeset by Tech-Set, Gateshead

Printed and bound in Great Britain at Scotprint, Haddington

The publisher's policy is to use paper manufactured from sustainable forests.

Picture Credits
The publisher would like to thank the following for their kind permission to reproduce their photographs:
(Key: b-bottom; c-centre; l-left; r-right; t-top)

2 Corbis: Paul Souders. **7 Alamy Images:** Imagestate. **8 Jupiter Unlimited:** Bananastock. **11 DK Images:** Julian Baum. **16 iStockphoto. 18 Alamy Images:** Angela Hampton Picture Library. **19 Jupiter Unlimited. 20 iStockphoto:** Jasmin Awad. **21 iStockphoto:** Ashok Rodrigues. **22 iStockphoto:** Olga Mirenska (l) (r). **31 Alamy Images:** Jim Wileman. **33 iStockphoto. 41 Alamy Images:** Helene Rogers (r). **iStockphoto:** Victor Burnside (l). **44 Alamy Images:** Jeff Morgan Cyprus. **46 iStockphoto:** Yegor Korzh. **47 Pearson Education Ltd. 48 DK Images:** Tim Ridley. **50 DK Images:** (t); Andy Crawford (b). **51 Alamy Images:** Paul Rapson. **56 iStockphoto:** Stefan Hermans. **61 DK Images:** Cecile Treal and Jean-Michel Ruiz. **62 DK Images:** Steve Gorton. **64 iStockphoto:** David Hughes (b); Katherine Moffitt (t). **66 PunchStock:** Digital Vision. **73 Alamy Images:** Stuart Kelly (r). **Corbis:** Ramin Talaie (l). **74 Alamy Images:** Simon Holdcroft Photography (l). **Rex Features:** Brian Harris (r). **75 Corbis:** TH-Foto / zefa (l). **iStockphoto:** Phill Danze (r). **79 iStockphoto:** Leslie Banks. **83 DK Images:** (r). **92 DK Images:** Caroline Mardon. **93 Art Directors and TRIP photo Library:** (b). **DK Images:** Peter Anderson (t). **iStockphoto:** Norlito Gumapac (c). **94 Alamy Images:** James Royall. **95 Pearson Education Ltd. 100 Jupiter Unlimited:** Liquidlibrary. **102 Jupiter Unlimited:** Comstock. **103 iStockphoto:** Richard Stanley. **114 iStockphoto:** Irina Behr. **117 iStockphoto:** Amanda Lewis

Cover images: *Front:* **iStockphoto:** Yusuf Anil Akduygu

All other images © Pearson Education

Picture Research by: Kevin Brown

Every effort has been made to trace the copyright holders and we apologise in advance for any unintentional omissions. We would be pleased to insert the appropriate acknowledgement in any subsequent edition of this publication.

Contents

N5.1 Powers and roots — 1
1 Integer powers of numbers — 1
2 Estimating square roots — 2
3 Prime factor decomposition — 3

A5.1 Sequences and graphs — 4
1 Generating sequences — 4
2 Making generalisations — 5
3 Using computers — 5
4 Sketching linear graphs — 6
5 Rearranging linear equations — 7
6 Graphs using real-life contexts — 8

G5.1 Measures and mensuration — 9
1 Perimeter and area — 9
2 Finding π — 10
3 Area of a circle — 11
4 Solving circle problems and using π — 12
5 Volume of prisms — 13
6 Surface area of prisms — 14

N5.2 Proportional reasoning — 15
1 Adding and subtracting fractions — 15
2 Multiplying fractions — 16
3 Dividing fractions — 17
4 Percentage change — 18
5 Ratio — 19
6 Direct proportion — 21

S5.1 Enquiry 1 — 23
1 Stem-and-leaf diagrams — 23
2 Starting a statistical investigation 1 — 24
3 Completing a statistical investigation 1 — 25
4 Data collection sheets — 27
5 Starting a statistical investigation 2 — 27
6 Completing a statistical investigation 2 — 29

A5.2 Equations and formulae — 31
1 Multiplying out brackets — 31
2 Factorising expressions — 32
3 Substituting into formulae — 32
4 Changing the subject of a formula — 33
5 Solving linear equations — 34
6 Trial and improvement — 34

G5.2 2D and 3D shapes — 35
1 Exploring angles and lines — 35
2 Solving problems — 36
3 Solving longer problems — 37
4 Drawing 3D objects — 38
5 Drawing plans and elevations — 39
6 More plans and elevations — 40
7 Solving problems using surface area and volume — 41
8 Surface area and volume of prisms — 42

N5.3 Calculations and calculators — 43
1 Powers of 10 — 43
2 Rounding and approximation — 44
3 Mental calculations with decimals — 45
4 Written calculations with decimals — 46
5 Using a calculator — 47
6 Problems involving measures — 48

S5.2 Probability 1 — 50
1 Simple probability — 50
2 Equally likely outcomes with two events — 50
3 Mutually exclusive events — 51
4 Practical probability experiments — 52
5 Simulating probability experiments — 53

A5.3 Functions and graphs — 54
1 Generating linear graphs using ICT — 54
2 Sketching graphs — 54
3 Drawing accurate graphs — 55
4 Direct proportion — 56
5 Reflecting graphs in $y = x$ — 57
6 Simple quadratic graphs using ICT — 58

G5.3 Transformations — 59
1 Planes of symmetry — 59
2 Combined transformations — 60
3 Islamic patterns — 61
4 Enlargements — 62
5 Enlargements in real-life applications — 63
6 Length, area and volume — 65

A5.4 Using algebra | **66**
1 Using graphs to solve problems | 66
2 Using algebra in geometry problems | 67
3 Using algebra in investigations | 68

S5.3 Enquiry 2 | **69**
1 Calculating statistics | 69
2 Line graphs for time series | 70
3 Scatter graphs | 71
4 Collecting and organising data | 72
5 Analysing and representing data | 74
6 Interpreting data | 75
7 Reporting and evaluating | 77

G5.4 Angles and constructions | **78**
1 Angles in polygons | 78
2 Regular polygons | 79
3 Regular polygons and the circle | 80
4 Angle problems and polygons | 81
5 Polygons and parallel lines | 82
6 Constructions | 83
7 Constructing triangles | 84
8 Loci | 85
9 More loci | 86

A5.5 Equations, formulae and graphs | **88**
1 Factorising | 88
2 Working with algebraic fractions | 89
3 Working with formulae | 89
4 Forming equations | 90
5 Visualising graphs | 91

6 Interpreting graphs | 91
7 Matching graphs to real-life situations | 92
8 Using graphs to solve problems | 93

S5.4 Probability 2 | **94**
1 Theoretical and experimental probability | 94
2 Mutually exclusive events | 95
3 Using experimental probability | 96
4 Choice or chance? | 97

N5.4 Solving problems | **98**
1 History of our number system and zero | 98
2 Number puzzles based on 3 by 3 grids | 99
3 Exploring fractions | 100
4 Problems involving properties of numbers | 101
5 Using algebra and counter-examples | 102

R5.1 Revision unit 1 | **104**
1 Using a calculator | 104
2 Using percentages to compare proportions | 104
3 Sequences, equations and graphs | 106
4 Angles and polygons | 108
5 Charts and diagrams | 109

R5.2 Revision unit 2 | **111**
1 Ratio and proportion | 111
2 Solving number problems | 113
3 Expressions, equations and formulae | 114
4 Circles and enlargements | 116
5 Probability | 118

Powers and roots

TASK 1: Integer powers of numbers

⊙ Points to remember

- The number 2 raised to the power 4 is 2^4 or $2 \times 2 \times 2 \times 2$.
  4 is called the **index** or **power**, and 2^4 is written in **index form**.
- To multiply numbers in index form, add the indices,
  so $a^m \times a^n = a^{m+n}$.
- To divide numbers in index form, subtract the indices,
  so $a^m \div a^n = a^{m-n}$.
- A negative number raised to an even power is positive.
  A negative number raised to an odd power is negative.

① Simplify these.

   a $3^9 \times 3^2$ **b** 2×2^5 **c** $11^2 \times 11^{-3}$ **d** $x^3 \times x^3$

   e $4^5 \div 4^2$ **f** $10^7 \div 10^3$ **g** $8^4 \div 8^{-6}$ **h** $z^3 \div z^2$

② Some numbers can be written as the sum of two cubes, for example:

$$152 = 5^3 + 3^3$$

Write each of these numbers as the sum of two cubes.

   a 28   **b** 72   **c** 1125

③ Look at this puzzle. Each ✶ stands for a missing digit.

$$(✶2)^2 = ✶✶✶$$

This has two possible solutions: $12^2 = 144$ or $22^2 = 484$.
The next possibility, $32^2 = 1024$, has too many digits on the right-hand side.

Now solve these puzzles. Write all the possible answers.

   a $(✶5)^2 = ✶✶✶$ **b** $(✶✶)^2 = ✶✶1$

   c $(✶)^3 = ✶✶6$ **d** $(✶✶)^3 = ✶✶✶7$

TASK 2: Estimating square roots

> ## ⦿ Points to remember
>
> ⊙ $\sqrt{n}$ is the **square root** of n.
>
> **Example** $\sqrt{81} = \pm 9$
>
> ⊙ You can find positive square roots on a calculator.
>
> **Example** To find $\sqrt{81}$, press: [8][1][√] or [√][8][1].
>
> Answer: 9
>
> ⊙ $\sqrt[3]{n}$ is the **cube root** of n, for example $\sqrt[3]{125} = 5$, $\sqrt[3]{-27} = -3$.
>
> ⊙ Some calculators have a **cube root** key [³√].
>
> **Example** To find $\sqrt[3]{64}$, press: [6][4][³√] or [³√][6][4].
>
> Answer: 4
>
> ⊙ For other roots there is a key like [ˣ√], or other variations.
>
> **Example** To find the value of $\sqrt[5]{32}$, key in [3][2][ˣ√][5].
>
> Answer: 2

1 **Use your calculator** to work these out.
   Where appropriate, give your answer correct to two decimal places.

   a $\sqrt[3]{6859}$ b $\sqrt[4]{6561}$ c $\sqrt[5]{59\,049}$ d $\sqrt[6]{15\,625}$

   e $\sqrt[3]{13\,824}$ f $\sqrt[8]{256}$ g $\sqrt[4]{5643}$ h $\sqrt[3]{76}$

2 The area of this square photograph frame is 352 cm².

   Use trial and improvement to find the length of one side.
   Give your answer to one decimal place.

3 Estimate the integer that is closest to the value of each of these.

   a $\sqrt[3]{26}$ b $\sqrt[3]{85}$ c $\sqrt[3]{200}$ d $\sqrt[3]{900}$

TASK 3: Prime factor decomposition

Points to remember

- Writing a number as the product of its prime factors is its **prime factor decomposition**.
  Example $24 = 2 \times 2 \times 2 \times 3$ or $2^3 \times 3$

- You can use different methods to find the prime factors of a number.

  The ladder method

  The prime factors of 24 are
  $3 \times 2 \times 2 \times 2 = 3 \times 2^3$.

  $$
  \begin{array}{c|c}
  3 & 24 \\
  2 & 8 \\
  2 & 4 \\
  2 & 2 \\
  \hline & 1
  \end{array}
  $$

  The tree method

  The prime factors of 200 are
  $5 \times 5 \times 2 \times 2 \times 2 = 5^2 \times 2^3$.

  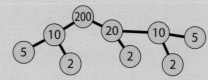

- The **highest common factor** (HCF) of a pair of numbers is the largest number that is a factor of each number.

  For example, $8 = 2 \times 2 \times 2$ and $12 = 2 \times 2 \times 3$.
  The highest common factor is 2×2.

- The **lowest common multiple** (LCM) of a pair of numbers is the smallest number that is a multiple of each number.

  For example, $8 = 2 \times 2 \times 2$ and $12 = 2 \times 2 \times 3$.
  The lowest common multiple of 8 and 12 is $2 \times 2 \times 2 \times 3 = 48$.

---

1. Use the ladder method to find the prime factors of:
   a 168
   b 243

2. Use the tree method to find the prime factors of:
   a 450
   b 595

3. What is the biggest number that is a factor of both 360 and 225?

4. What is the smallest number that is a multiple of both 72 and 117?

5. The three numbers missing from the boxes are different prime numbers greater than 3.

   $$\square \times \square \times \square = 1547$$

   What are the three prime numbers?

Sequences and graphs

TASK 1: Generating sequences

 Points to remember

⊙ A sequence of numbers follows a rule.

⊙ You can generate a sequence if you know the first term and the **term-to-term rule**.

⊙ You can also generate a sequence if you know the formula for the nth term. This is called the **position-to-term rule**.

⊙ A **linear sequence** has the same difference between consecutive terms.

① Write the first five terms of each sequence.

	1st term	**Term-to-term rule**
a	1	add 6
b	6	subtract 7
c	9	multiply by 3
d	0	multiply by 7 and add 2
e	−2	add 5 and multiply by 2
f	5	multiply by 3 and subtract 4
g	256	divide by 2
h	3	subtract 5 and multiply by 4

② Each expression is the nth term of a sequence.
Use it to generate the first five terms for the sequence.

a $5n$ **b** $2n + 10$

c $4n - 3$ **d** $3n + 9$

e $n + 16$ **f** $7n - 4$

g $8n + 1$ **h** $5n - 8$

i $9n + 4$ **j** $85 - 2n$

TASK 2: Making generalisations

⊙ Points to remember

⊙ A **linear sequence** has the same difference between consecutive terms.

⊙ To find the formula for the nth term of a linear sequence, work out the difference between consecutive terms. This gives you the coefficient of n.

1 Work out the difference between each term of these sequences.
Use the difference to work out the formula for the nth term.
In each case, check that your answer is correct.

a 5, 8, 11, 14, 17, ...

b 1, 5, 9, 13, 17, ...

c 10, 12, 14, 16, 18, ...

d 9, 15, 21, 27, 33, ...

e 3, 10, 17, 24, 31, ...

f −4, −1, 2, 5, 8, ...

g 6, 17, 28, 39, 50, ...

h 8, 18, 28, 38, 48, ...

i 0.5, 1, 1.5, 2, 2.5, ...

j $\frac{3}{5}$, $\frac{4}{5}$, $\frac{5}{5}$, $\frac{6}{5}$, $\frac{7}{5}$, ...

TASK 3: Using computers

⊙ Points to remember

⊙ You can generate a sequence on a spreadsheet using the term-to-term rule or the formula for the nth term.

⊙ The spreadsheet speeds up working out terms of a sequence.

⊙ When the position and term of a linear sequence are plotted as pairs of coordinates, the points lie on a straight line.

1 a A spreadsheet is set up with this sequence.
The first term is in cell A2.
What cell will the 100th term be in?

b What is the term-to-term rule of the sequence?

c What is the formula for the nth term of the sequence?

d What is the 100th term of the sequence?.

	A
1	**Sequence**
2	7
3	11
4	15
5	19
6	23
7	27
8	31
9	35
10	39
11	43
12	47
13	52

(2) **a** Draw a table with columns for 'Position' and 'Term'.
Use it to record the coordinates of the points on this graph.

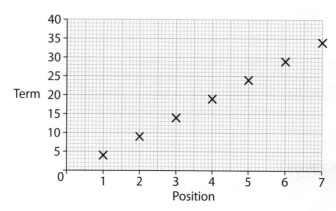

b Use the table to work out the formula for the nth term of the sequence.

TASK 4: Sketching linear graphs

 Points to remember

⊙ The equation $y = 5x - 4$ is in the form $y = ax + b$.
The gradient of its straight-line graph is 5.
The intercept on the y-axis is $(0, -4)$.

⊙ A sketch of a graph is a neat drawing showing some of the features that can be seen from its equation. Label the axes and mark the origin and the point where the line crosses the y-axis.

(1) Write the equations of these linear graphs.

   a Gradient 2, intercept $(0, 10)$ **b** Gradient 5, intercept $(0, -4)$

   c Gradient -4, intercept $(0, 9)$ **d** Gradient -2, intercept $(0, -2)$

   e Gradient 8, intercept $(0, 1)$ **f** Gradient 0.5, intercept $(0, 3)$

   g Gradient -5, intercept $(0, -7)$ **h** Gradient 6, intercept $(0, -4)$

   i Gradient 1, intercept $(0, 18)$ **j** Gradient -7, intercept $(0, -9)$

Make a sketch of each graph.

TASK 5: Rearranging linear equations

Points to remember

⊙ The equation of a straight line is normally given in the form $y = ax + b$.

⊙ The number a, the coefficient of x, gives the gradient of the straight-line graph of the equation, and the number b gives the intercept on the y-axis.

⊙ If a linear equation is in a different form, you can rearrange it to the normal form.

(1) Rearrange these equations in the form $y = ax + b$.

a $y - 3x = 0$ b $y - 2x = 8$

c $y - 7x = 11$ d $y + 3x = 5$

e $y - x = 10$ f $y - 4x = -15$

g $2x + y = 6$ h $3x + y = 14$

i $2 = y - x$ j $1 = y + 5x$

(2) Write down the gradient of the graph and the intercept for these equations.

a $y - 9x = 0$ b $y - 7x = 8$

c $y - x = -1$ d $y - 8x = 6$

e $y + 2x = -8$ f $y - 3.5x = -9$

g $6.5x + y = -21$ h $11x + y = 3$

i $6 = y - x$ j $y + 4x - 7 = 0$

TASK 6: Graphs using real-life contexts

Points to remember

⊙ When you read information from a graph of a real-life context, check the scales and units on the axes.

1 Study this graph converting British pounds to Chinese yuan.

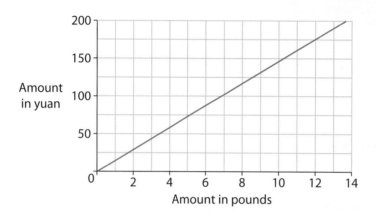

a Estimate the number of Chinese yuan to one pound.

b Estimate the number of pounds to 100 yuan.

c Li Ming is a TV presenter.
She is travelling to England.
She wants to exchange 3000 yuan.
Estimate how many pounds this is.

d Li Ming is presenting a holiday programme for Chinese people. She needs to convert the cost of travel and hotel accommodation from pounds to yuan. Estimate these costs.

  i Air fare: £750

 ii Hotel: £350

iii Eating out: £175

 iv Bus travel: £55

Chinese bank notes

Measures and mensuration

TASK 1: Perimeter and area

> ### ⊙ Points to remember
>
> - **Area of a rectangle** = base × height
> - **Area of a triangle** = $\frac{1}{2}$ × base × perpendicular height
> - **Area of a parallelogram** = base × perpendicular height
> - **Area of a trapezium** = $\frac{1}{2}$ × sum of parallel sides × perpendicular height
> - Area is measured in square units.
> - When you work out the perimeter or area of a shape, make sure that the sides are in the same units.

You may **use a calculator**. Show your working.

1. Find the area of each shape.

   a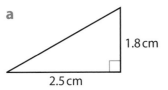

   b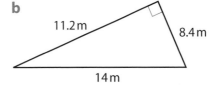

   c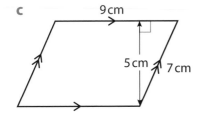

   d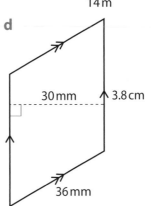

2. A triangle has a total area of 144 mm². The base is 12 mm long. What is the perpendicular height of the triangle?

3. A parallelogram has an area of 36 cm².
   a The two longer sides are a perpendicular height of 4.5 cm apart. How long is the base?
   b The two shorter sides are 9 cm long. How far apart are they?

4 A table top is in the shape of a trapezium.

Calculate the area of the table top in square metres.

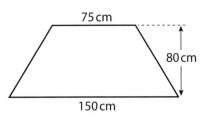

5 Find the area of each shape.

a

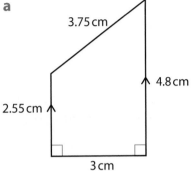

b

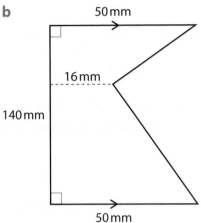

TASK 2: Finding π

Points to remember

⊙ The **circumference of a circle** is $\pi \times$ diameter.

⊙ The **diameter of a circle** is circumference $\div \pi$.

⊙ π is a little bit more than 3. Approximations for π are $\frac{22}{7}$ and 3.14.

You may **use a calculator**. Show your working.

1 Work out the circumference of circles with these diameters.

    a 15 cm   **b** 75 mm   **c** 1 m   **d** 9.3 km

2 Work out the diameter of circles with these circumferences.

    a 15 cm   **b** 75 mm   **c** 1 m   **d** 9.3 km

(3) Mars has a circumference of approximately 21 300 km.
How big is its diameter?

Mars

(4) Mercury is 57 910 000 km away from the Sun.
One complete orbit takes about 88 days.

How far does Mercury travel in one complete orbit?

(5) A **mnemonic** makes information easier to memorise.

One mnemonic to remember the digits of π was composed by Anna Beedham,
aged 82. The number of letters in each word gives the first 15 digits of π in order.

Can I have a phone connected to Rhona's house and maybe
tomorrow reconnect Joanne's phoneline?

What are the first 15 digits of π?

TASK 3: Area of a circle

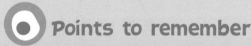 **Points to remember**

⊙ The **area of a circle** is $\pi \times$ radius $\times$ radius $= \pi \times (\text{radius})^2 = \pi r^2$

⊙ The area of a circle is measured in square units.

Use a calculator for these questions.

(1) Calculate the area of circles with these radii.

   a 9.3 mm   **b** 15.8 cm   **c** 0.03 m   **d** 30 mm

(2) Calculate the area of circles with these diameters.

   a 18 cm   **b** 25.8 mm   **c** 4.42 km   **d** 30 mm

(3) Which has the biggest total area:
a circle with a radius of 8 cm or four separate identical circles each with a radius
of 2 cm?
Show your working.

TASK 4: Solving circle problems and using π

Points to remember

- The **circumference of a circle** is $\pi \times$ diameter.
- The **diameter of a circle** is circumference $\div$ π.
- π is a little bit more than 3. Approximations for π are $\frac{22}{7}$ and 3.14.
- The **area of a circle** is $\pi \times$ radius $\times$ radius $= \pi \times$ (radius)$^2 = \pi r^2$.
- The area of a circle is measured in square units.

1. An annulus is a ring formed from two circles with the same centre.

   Calculate the area of this annulus.

   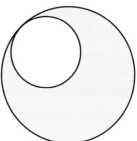

2. The shaded shape is formed from two circles.

   The larger circle has a radius of 18 cm.
   The smaller circle a radius of 9 cm.

   Calculate the area of the shaded shape.

   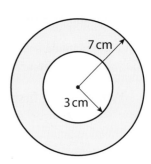

3. The diagram shows a 12 mm square drawn around a circle with diameter 12 mm.

   The circle just touches the square.

   Calculate the shaded area.

   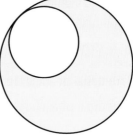

4. The diagram shows a square with side 12 mm enclosing four identical circles.

   Calculate the shaded area.

   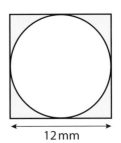

TASK 5: Volume of prisms

  Points to remember

- A **prism** is a 3D shape with two parallel end faces of the same size and shape, and rectangular side faces. It has the same cross-section throughout its length.
- The formula for the **volume of a prism** is:
  Volume = cross-sectional area $\times$ length = $A \times l$
- Volume is measured in cubic units.

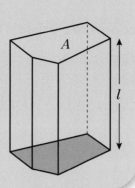

① Calculate the volume of each cuboid.

a

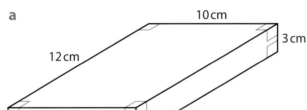

b

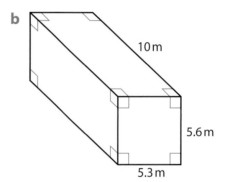

② Calculate the volume of each prism.

a

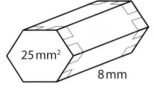

b

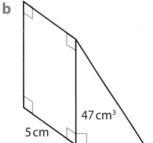

c

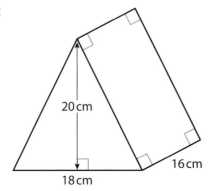

d

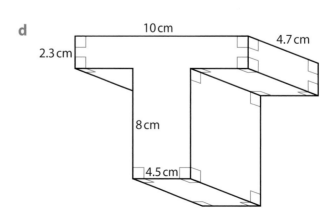

TASK 6: Surface area of prisms

Points to remember

- The **surface area of a prism** is the sum of the areas of all the faces.
- Surface area is measured in square units.

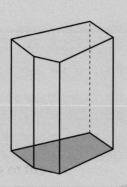

1. Calculate the surface area of each of these prisms.

a

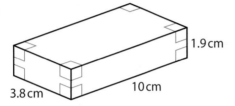

1.9 cm
10 cm
3.8 cm

b

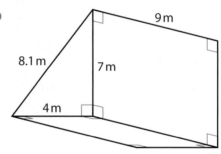

9 m
8.1 m
7 m
4 m

c

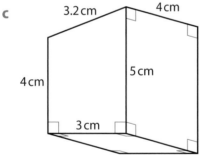

3.2 cm   4 cm
5 cm
4 cm
3 cm

d

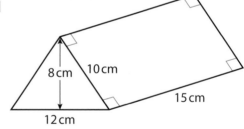

8 cm   10 cm
12 cm   15 cm

2. The total surface area of a cuboid container is 184 m².

The cuboid is 2 m high and 6 m wide.

How long is the cuboid?

Proportional reasoning

TASK 1: Adding and subtracting fractions

Points to remember

- To find a fraction equivalent to a given fraction, multiply or divide the numerator and denominator by the same number.
- To add and subtract fractions, they must have the same denominator.
- You can use your calculator to add and subtract fractions.

  For example, to work out $1\frac{3}{4} + 2\frac{4}{5}$, enter

  $\boxed{1}\boxed{a^b/_c}\boxed{3}\boxed{a^b/_c}\boxed{4}\boxed{+}\boxed{2}\boxed{a^b/_c}\boxed{4}\boxed{a^b/_c}\boxed{5}\boxed{=}$.

  The display should show something like $\boxed{4\lrcorner11\lrcorner20}$.

1. Choose from these fractions.

   $\left(\frac{2}{3}\right)$ $\left(\frac{4}{5}\right)$ $\left(\frac{1}{2}\right)$ $\left(\frac{3}{4}\right)$ $\left(\frac{5}{6}\right)$

   Copy and complete these.

   a $\bigcirc + \bigcirc = 1\frac{1}{4}$

   b $\bigcirc - \bigcirc = \frac{1}{30}$

   c $\bigcirc + \bigcirc + \bigcirc = 1\frac{11}{12}$

   d $\bigcirc + \bigcirc + \bigcirc = 2\frac{1}{20}$

   e $\bigcirc + \bigcirc + \bigcirc = 2\frac{2}{15}$

   f $\bigcirc + \bigcirc + \bigcirc = 2\frac{3}{10}$

   g $\bigcirc + \bigcirc + \bigcirc = 2\frac{1}{4}$

   h $\bigcirc + \bigcirc - \bigcirc = 1\frac{1}{20}$

2. John walked from home $\frac{3}{4}$ of a mile to the bus stop.

   He travelled on the bus to the town centre for $3\frac{7}{8}$ miles.

   How far is John's home from the town centre?

3. A magazine has two adverts on the same page.

   The first advert uses $\frac{1}{8}$ of the page. The second advert uses $\frac{1}{6}$ of the page.

   What fraction of the whole page is not covered by adverts?

TASK 2: Multiplying fractions

Example

$$\frac{21}{40} \times \frac{15}{28} = \frac{\overset{3}{\cancel{21}}}{\underset{8}{\cancel{40}}} \times \frac{\overset{3}{\cancel{15}}}{\underset{4}{\cancel{28}}}$$ Cancel the 21 and 28 by 7, and the 15 and 40 by 5.

$$= \frac{3 \times 3}{8 \times 4}$$ Multiply the numerators and multiply the denominators.

$$= \frac{9}{32}$$

Work these out **without a calculator**. Show your working.

1. a $\frac{5}{6} \times \frac{2}{15}$ b $\frac{6}{15} \times \frac{5}{18}$ c $\frac{2}{3} \times \frac{9}{16}$

   d $\frac{14}{33} \times \frac{11}{21}$ e $1\frac{3}{5} \times 2\frac{1}{2}$ f $3\frac{1}{3} \times 1\frac{7}{10}$

2. Sophie has a collection of videos.
   Two fifths of her videos are of football matches and
   five twelfths of these are Premier League.

   What fraction of Sophie's collection are Premier League football matches?

3. Two thirds of the chocolates in a box are milk chocolates.
   Of the milk chocolates, three quarters have nut centres.

   What fraction of the chocolates are milk with nut centres?

4. Four ninths of the cars in the car park are saloons.
   Three eighths of the saloons are silver.

   What fraction of the cars in the car park are silver saloons?

5. Hassan is trying to get fit.
   He spends three quarters of his free time at the gym, and
   two thirds of his time at the gym using weights.

   What fraction of his free time does Hassan spend using weights?

TASK 3: Dividing fractions

 Points to remember

⊙ You can use a calculator to multiply and divide fractions.

Example 1

To work out $\frac{2}{3} \times \frac{3}{5}$, enter ⌊2⌋⌊$a^b/_c$⌋⌊3⌋⌊×⌋⌊3⌋⌊$a^b/_c$⌋⌊5⌋⌊=⌋.

The display will show $\frac{2}{5}$, which will look something like:　　　⌐ 2⌐5 ⌐.

Example 2

To work out $\frac{2}{3} \div \frac{5}{6}$, enter ⌊2⌋⌊$a^b/_c$⌋⌊3⌋⌊÷⌋⌊5⌋⌊$a^b/_c$⌋⌊6⌋⌊=⌋.

The display will show $\frac{4}{5}$, which will look something like:　　　⌐ 4⌐5 ⌐.

---

① Try this puzzle.

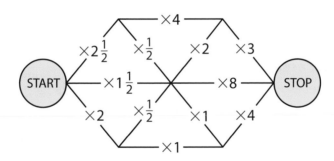

- ⊙ Start with 1 in your calculator display.
- ⊙ Choose a route from START to STOP. You may go along each line only once.
- ⊙ Multiply the number in your display by the number on the line.
- ⊙ Aim to finish with an answer of 6.

Record in your book the fractions that you multiplied to make 6.

② Now find three more ways to do it.

TASK 4: Percentage change

Points to remember

- To find 20%, find 10% by dividing by 10, then multiply by 2.
- You can find 30%, 40%, 50%, … in a similar way.
- If there is no quick way to find a percentage, first find 1%, then multiply by the percentage.
- Think carefully about which number to take as a whole.
- Always include any units in the answer.

Example

To find 65% of £82:

- You can calculate $\frac{65}{100}$ of £82:

  ⑥⑤÷①⓪⓪×⑧②=.

- Or you can use fewer keys to calculate 0.65 × 82:

  ⓪•⑥⑤×⑧②=.

① Karen's class had a maths test.
The total number of marks was 40.

Karen got 65%.
How many marks did she get?

② 1200 people took part in a survey about banks.
They were asked which bank they use.
36% of them said that they used an Internet banking service.
How many people was this?

③ Pritam pays £32.55 for some jeans.
The full price of the same jeans is £35.
What percentage discount did Pritam get on the full price?

(4) Dan had his bike stolen.
The insurance company paid 65% of the original value.
Dan got £156 from the insurance company.
How much did his bike cost originally?

(5) Beth earns £5.50 an hour as a waitress.
She gets a pay rise of 8%.
What is her new hourly rate of pay?

(6) Sandeep pays tax at 22%.
After tax he earns £117 per week.
How much does Sandeep earn each week before tax?

(7) All the pupils in a class have at least one cat or dog.
80% of them have a cat.
60% of them have a dog.
12 pupils have both a cat and a dog.

How many pupils are in the class?

TASK 5: Ratio

Points to remember

- Ratios are simplified like fractions.
- A **unitary ratio** is written in the form $1 : m$.
- To change $2 : 15$ to a unitary ratio, divide both sides by 2 to get $1 : 7.5$.
- When you divide a quantity in the ratio $3 : 7$, the smaller part is $\frac{3}{10}$ and the larger part is $\frac{7}{10}$ of the whole quantity.

Example 1

£28 is shared in the ratio $1 : 2 : 4$. How much is each share?

There are $1 + 2 + 4 = 7$ shares.
1 share: £28 ÷ 7 = £4
2 shares: £4 × 2 = £8
4 shares: £4 × 4 = £16

Check: £4 + £8 + £16 = £28

Example 2

Some money is divided into two shares in the ratio 3 : 4.
The smaller part is £15.
How much is the other part?

There are 3 + 4 = 7 shares altogether.
£15 is 3 shares.
1 share: £15 ÷ 3 = £5
4 shares: £5 × 4 = £20

Check: £15 : £20 = 3 : 4

---

1 Tin A has red paint and blue paint in the ratio 2 : 3.
Tin B has red paint and blue paint in the ratio 4 : 5.
Which tin has the greater proportion of blue paint?
Explain how you know.

2 65 pupils voted whether to go and see *Hamlet* or *Macbeth* at the theatre.
The result was a ratio of 10 : 3 in favour of *Hamlet*.
How many pupils voted for *Hamlet*?

3 A recipe for a fruit drink says:

'Mix 1 part lemon juice with 4 parts orange juice.'

Tom wants to make 1 litre of this fruit drink.
How many millilitres of orange juice should he use?

4 In 2007, City Football Club scored 21 goals at home.
The ratio of home goals to away goals was 7 : 5.
How many goals did the club score altogether?

5 **a** Tara has some pairs of earrings.
The ratio of her stud to drop earrings is 1 : 2.
Tara has 8 pairs of stud earrings.
How many pairs of drop earrings does she have?

b Emma also has some pairs of earrings.
Her ratio of stud to drop earrings is 2 : 3.
Emma has 12 pairs of drop earrings.
How many pairs of stud earrings does she have?

c Tara and Emma combine their sets of earrings.
What is the ratio of stud to drop earrings in the combined collection?

TASK 6: Direct proportion

● Points to remember

- ⊙ If the ratio of two quantities stays the same as they get bigger or smaller, they are in **direct proportion**.
- ⊙ When you solve direct proportion problems:
  - use the **unitary method** to make the value of one of the variables to 1;
  - make sure that related quantities are in the same units.

Example

The mass of 60 ml of olive oil is 45 g.
What is the mass of 108 ml of olive oil?

	Oil (ml)	Mass (g)
	60	45
÷ 60	1	0.75
× 108	108	81

108 ml of olive oil has a mass of 81 g.

Do these questions **without using a calculator**. Show your working.

1. 6 lollies cost £3.30.
   How much do 10 lollies cost?

2. Chocolate drops cost £1.85p for 150 g.
   What is the cost of 750 g of chocolate drops?

3. Lobster costs £6 for 90 g.
   How many grams of lobster can you buy for £15?

4. Four litres of paint cost £36.60.
   What is the cost of seven litres of the paint?

5.
   Cherry ice-cream
   0.5 litre cream
   1 kg cherries
   250 g sugar

   This recipe is for cherry ice-cream for 8 people.

   a Roger makes enough ice-cream for 12 people.
     How much cream does he use?

   b Mary makes ice-cream using 2.5 kg of cherries.
     How much sugar does she use?

(6) 8 km is approximately 5 miles.

   a Approximately how many miles are 50 km?

   b Approximately how many kilometres are 11 miles?

(7) Here is a photo of basketball players and its enlargement.

A different photo is 6 cm tall and 4.5 cm wide.
An enlargement of the photograph is 15 cm tall.
How wide is the enlarged photo?

Enquiry 1

TASK 1: Stem-and-leaf diagrams

● Points to remember

- A **stem-and-leaf diagram** shows data in order from lowest to highest. The data can be **discrete** or **continuous**.
- You can work out the **mode**, **median** and **range** directly from a stem-and-leaf diagram.
- You can draw a **grouped frequency diagram** from a stem-and-leaf diagram.

The **stem-and-leaf diagram** below shows the time to the nearest hour that 17 people watched TV in one week.

The mode of the times is 16 hours.
The median time is 23 hours.
The range is 32 − 6 = 26 hours.

```
0 | 6  8
1 | 2  6  6  6  8
2 | 3  3  5  5  6  6  8  9
3 | 0  8
```
Key: 2 | 5 means 25 hours

The data in the stem-and-leaf diagram is shown in this **frequency diagram**.

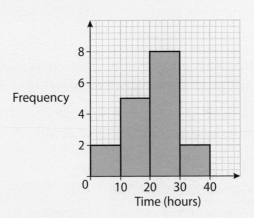

You will need some **graph paper**.

1. 30 pupils run a cross-country race.
   Their finishing times to the nearest minute are shown in the table.

12	14	14	16	16	19	20	21	21	23
23	24	24	24	25	25	25	25	25	26
27	27	29	29	30	33	34	36	41	45

   a Represent this information on a stem-and-leaf diagram.

   b Use the stem-and-leaf diagram to work out the mode and the median.

   c Use the stem-and-leaf diagram to work out the range.

d Copy and complete this grouped frequency table.

Time (*t* minutes)	Frequency
$0 \leqslant t < 10$	0
$10 \leqslant t < 20$	6

e Use the grouped frequency table to draw a grouped frequency diagram.

TASK 2: Starting a statistical investigation 1

 Points to remember

⊙ Make a **hypothesis** about what the results of the investigation might be.

⊙ To decide if your hypothesis is true, collect and analyse appropriate data.

⊙ You could order the data and draw a **stem-and-leaf diagram**.

The next few tasks are based on this word game.

Words are made from the letters in this grid.
Words must have three or more letters.

Each letter can be used only **once** in each word.
All words must contain the letter **M**.

Plurals are not allowed.

Points are scored as shown in this table.

The winner is the player with most points
after 1 minute.

T	E	N
S	M	T
E	T	A

Letters in word	Points per letter
3, 4 or 5	1
6 or 7	2
8 or 9	3

① Play the game and see how many points you can score in 1 minute.

② Leroy wants to investigate how well pupils in his school do in the game.
He decides to test this hypothesis on pupils in Year 9:

'Pupils who are in higher maths sets score more points in the game.'

Write some other hypotheses that Leroy could test in his investigation.
For each hypothesis list the data that Leroy needs to collect.

3 Leroy asked 15 Year 9 pupils in each of the top set and the middle set to play the game. The results are shown in these tables.

Year 9 middle set				
37	23	44	18	21
14	24	32	23	41
35	11	17	27	38

Year 9 top set				
32	35	24	58	27
19	35	28	43	14
35	31	27	38	48

Represent each set of data on a stem-and-leaf diagram.

TASK 3: Completing a statistical investigation 1

⊙ Points to remember

- ⊙ **Interpret** the data by comparing the spread (range) and average values (median, mode or mean) of the data sets.
- ⊙ Look for other **similarities or differences** between the sets of data.
- ⊙ **Draw a conclusion**. Decide if your original hypothesis is true or not.
- ⊙ **Evaluate** results. Decide whether there are further questions to explore.

1 **a** Leroy asked pupils in the middle and top sets in Year 10 to play a word game. These stem-and-leaf diagrams show the scores they obtained.

Year 10 middle set

```
1 | 7  8  8
2 | 3  3  3  6  8
3 | 3  8  9  9
4 | 0  5  9
```

Key: 2 | 1 means 21 points

Year 10 top set

```
1 | 8  9
2 | 0  6  9
3 | 4  4  4  8
4 | 3  8  8
5 | 2  3
6 | 2
```

Key: 2 | 4 means 24 points

Copy and complete this table.

	Year 10 middle set	Year 10 top set
Median		
Mode		
Range		

b Write sentences comparing the average and spread for each set of scores.

c Write sentences describing other similarities or differences between the sets of scores.

d Leroy's hypothesis was:

'Pupils who are in higher maths sets score more points in the game.'

Is Leroy's hypothesis true or false? Explain your answer.

2 **a** Leroy asked some pupils in Year 8 and in Year 11 to play the game. These stem-and-leaf diagrams show the scores they obtained.

Year 8

```
1 | 7  8  8
2 | 3  3  3  6
3 | 3  8  9  9
4 | 0  5  9
5 | 2
```

Key: 2 | 1 means 21 points

Year 11

```
1 | 8  9
2 | 0  9
3 | 6  6  8
4 | 0  5  8  9
5 | 2  3
6 | 5  6
```

Key: 2 | 4 means 24 points

Copy and complete this table.

	Year 8	Year 11
Median		
Mode		
Range		

b Write some sentences comparing the average and spread for each set of scores.

c Write sentences describing other similarities or differences between the sets of scores.

d Leroy's hypothesis was:

'Older pupils score more points in the game.'

Is Leroy's hypothesis true or false? Explain your answer.

TASK 4: Data collection sheets

Points to remember

⊙ Make sure that the data you collect is relevant to your hypothesis.

⊙ Collect continuous data in groups that span the range of the data. These groups are called **class intervals**.

⊙ Choose class intervals so that the number of groups is neither too small nor too large. In most situations, aim for 5 to 7 groups.

Look at the word game in Task 2. This task is based on the same game.

1 John decided to investigate the word game described in Task 2.

He decides to test all three of these hypotheses:

'Pupils who are in higher maths sets score more points in the game.'

'Older pupils score more points in the game.'

'Boys score more points than girls.'

Design a data collection sheet that would enable John to collect the data he needs.

2 Fay is in Year 7.
She is in the top set for maths and scores 30 points in the game.

Sadiq is in Year 9.
He is in the middle set for maths and scores 42 points.

Record the data for Fay and Sadiq in the data collection sheet you designed for question **1**.

TASK 5: Starting a statistical investigation 2

Points to remember

⊙ Base your investigation on a hypothesis about what the results might be.

⊙ Collect continuous data in **grouped frequency tables**.

⊙ Continuous data can be represented in a **grouped frequency diagram**.

You will need some graph paper.

Words are made from the letters in this grid.
Words must have three or more letters.

Each letter can be used only **once** in each word.
All words must contain the letter **E**.

Plurals are not allowed.

Points are scored as shown in this table.
The winner is the first to score 30 points.

L	A	N
S	E	H
E	T	P

Letters in word	Points per letter
3, 4 or 5	1
6 or 7	2
8 or 9	3

(1) Play this game. Time how long it takes you to score 30 points.

(2) Aisha decided to test this hypothesis on pupils in Year 9:

'Pupils in higher maths sets score 30 points in a shorter time.'

She asked 30 pupils in each of two Year 9 classes to play the game.
Their times in seconds to score 30 points are shown in these tables.

Class A					
37	23	44	58	45	26
24	24	52	24	20	26
35	19	67	45	52	30
65	27	32	33	32	18
43	31	27	27	26	43

Class B					
24	42	25	32	22	35
43	30	58	44	36	49
44	27	36	25	48	29
38	55	37	39	30	68
25	48	45	32	26	28

a   Make a grouped frequency table like this for each set of data.

Time (t seconds)	Tally	Frequency
$10 \leqslant t < 20$		
$20 \leqslant t < 30$		

b   Draw a grouped frequency diagram for each set of data.

TASK 6: Completing a statistical investigation 2

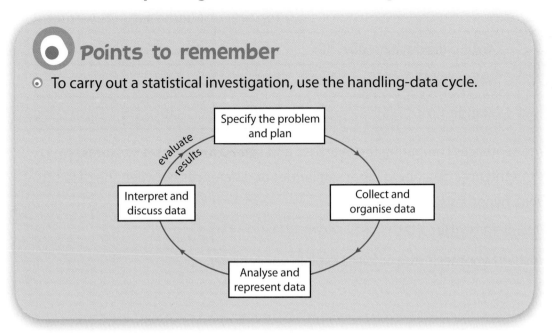

Points to remember

⊙ To carry out a statistical investigation, use the handling-data cycle.

This task is based on the same word game as in Task 5.

1 **a** Aisha recorded the time it took pupils in Year 10 to score 30 points.
She represented this data in these frequency diagrams.

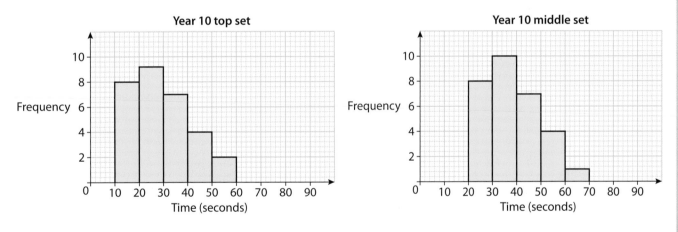

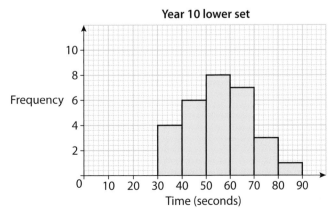

Use the frequency diagrams to copy and complete this table.

		Top set	Middle set	Lower set
Average	Group in which median lies			
	Modal class			
Spread	Range	40	40	50

b Write sentences comparing the averages and spread for each set of scores.

c Write sentences describing other similarities or differences between the data sets.

d Aisha's hypothesis was:

'Pupils in higher maths sets score 30 points in a shorter time.'

Is Aisha's hypothesis true or false? Explain your answer.

Equations and formulae

TASK 1: Multiplying out brackets

⊙ Points to remember

- When you multiply out a bracket, remember to multiply each term.

  Example $6(3x - 5) = 18x - 30$

- Multiplying a bracket by a negative number changes the sign of each term in the bracket.

  Example $-4(2x - 3) = -8x + 12$

- You can simplify an expression by multiplying out the brackets and collecting like terms.

1. Multiply out the brackets.

   a $9(x + 7)$ b $6(x - 4)$ c $5(3x + 8)$

   d $9(6x - 3)$ e $8(7x - 5)$ f $7(9x + 10)$

   g $-3(2x - 10)$ h $-4(2x + 11)$

2. Simplify these expressions.

   a $3(7x - 1) + 5(2x + 6)$ b $9(3x - 4) + 5(2x + 3)$

   c $8(5x - 7) + 7(4x + 1)$ d $2(5x - 1) + 7(3x + 6)$

   e $4(4x - 5) - 9(x - 1)$ f $11(3x + 5) - 6(2x + 3)$

   g $-3(x - 1) - 2(5x + 4)$ h $-4(6x - 3) + 5(9x + 2)$

TASK 2: Factorising expressions

⊙ Points to remember

- You can factorise an expression by removing the **highest common factor**.

  Example $16x + 28 = 4(4x + 7)$

- You can simplify an expression by multiplying out the brackets, collecting like terms and factorising if possible.

- Multiplying out brackets and factorising are opposite actions.

(1)   Factorise these expressions.

    a $36x + 54y$ **b** $35a - 45b$

    c $90m - 50n$ **d** $28w - 21x$

    e $27ax + 45ay$ **f** $20bp - 28bq$

    g $14pq + 21qr$ **h** $15n^2 - 25n$

(2)   Simplify these expressions.

    a $3(7x - 1) - 5(2x + 6)$ **b** $9(3x - 4) - 5(2x + 3)$

    c $8(5x - 7) - 7(4x + 1)$ **d** $4(5x - 1) + 8(3x + 7)$

    e $10(2x - 3) - 5(x - 1)$ **f** $6(3x + 5) - 4(2x + 3)$

TASK 3: Substituting into formulae

⊙ Points to remember

- A **formula** is a way of describing a rule or relationship. A formula can be written using algebraic expressions. It must have an $=$ sign.

- When you substitute values into a formula always check that you are using the correct units.

(1)   The formula for the area of a triangle is $A = \frac{1}{2}bh$, where A is the area, b is the length of the base and h the perpendicular height.

    Find the area of a triangle with $b = 12$ cm and $h = 59$ mm.

2 The formula to convert temperature measured in degrees Celsius to degrees Fahrenheit is $F = \frac{9}{5}C + 32$, where F is the temperature in Fahrenheit and C the temperature in Celsius.

Use the formula to work out F when $C = 42\,°C$.

3 The formula $d = st$ calculates the distances travelled when travelling at constant speed s for time t.

Work out the distance travelled when $s = 70\,$mph and $t = 24$ minutes.

4 The formula for the volume of a cuboid is $V = lwh$, where V is the volume, l the length of the base, w the width of the base and h the height of the cuboid.

Work out the volume when $l = 5\,$cm, $w = 7\,$cm and $h = 25\,$mm.

5 The formula for the volume of a triangular prism is $V = \frac{1}{2}bhl$, where V is the volume, b the length of the base of the triangle, h the perpendicular height of the triangle and l the length of the prism.

Use the formula to find V when $b = 5\,$cm, $h = 60\,$mm and $l = 20\,$cm.

TASK 4: Changing the subject of a formula

 Points to remember

⊙ In the formula $A = lw$, A is called the **subject** of the formula.

⊙ You can rearrange a formula to make a different letter its subject.

For example, the formula $A = lw$ can also be written as $l = \dfrac{A}{w}$ or $w = \dfrac{A}{l}$.

1 Make the letter in brackets the subject of each formula.

a $P = qr$ (q) b $M = l + w$ (w)

c $A = bh$ (h) d $y = x - 5$ (x)

e $V = Ah$ (h) f $A = 2\pi r$ (r)

g $y = wx$ (x) h $y = 2 - x$ (x)

i $y = x + w$ (x) j $V = rph$ (h)

TASK 5: Solving linear equations

Points to remember

- When you solve equations, what you do to one side of the equation you must do to the other.
- If necessary, rearrange the equation so that all the terms with the unknown letter are on one side.
- Check your solutions to equations by substituting the value back in the original equation.

1 Find the value of x in each equation.
Check your answers by substituting the value of x back into the equation.

   a $9x + 13 = 49$ **b** $7x - 3 = 39$

   c $11x + 9 = 64$ **d** $4x + 14 = 62$

   e $3(7x - 5) = 132$ **f** $8(3 + 7x) = 136$

   g $121 = 5x + 7(2x + 1)$ **h** $6(8x + 3) - 5(4x + 7) = 39$

2 Find the value of x in each equation.

   a $9x + 5 = 7x + 11$ **b** $6x + 4 = x + 14$

   c $10x - 3 = 5x + 2$ **d** $12x - 9 = 8x + 7$

   e $6x + 11 = 7x + 6$ **f** $8x + 3 = 10x - 1$

TASK 6: Trial and improvement

Points to remember

- You can use **trial and improvement** to solve non-linear equations.
- Trial and improvement is a step-by-step method that starts with an estimate and gradually improves the answer with each step.
- A graph can help you find a first estimate.

Use your calculator and trial and improvement.

1 Find one positive and one negative solution for each equation.
Give your answers to two decimal places.

   a $x^2 - x = 7$ **b** $x^2 + 3x = 17$

2D and 3D shapes

TASK 1: Exploring angles and lines

Points to remember

- Angles on a straight line add to 180°.
- **Vertically opposite angles** are equal.
- Pairs of **corresponding angles** on parallel lines are equal.
- Pairs of **alternate angles** on parallel lines are equal.
- The interior angles of a triangle add to 180°.
- The interior angles of an n-sided polygon add to $(n - 2) \times 180°$.

Example

Calculate the size of angle a.

Angle $b = 131°$ (angles on a straight line)

Angle $a = 131°$ (alternate angles)

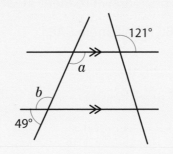

① Work out the angles labelled a to g in the diagrams below.

Show your working. State which angle facts you use at each stage.

a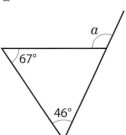

b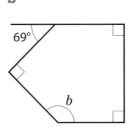

c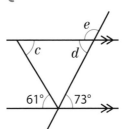

d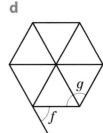

regular hexagon

TASK 2: Solving problems

 Points to remember

⊙ Read the question carefully and draw a diagram.

⊙ Use information given in the question to label the diagram. Look for:
  - equal angles;
  - equal lengths.

⊙ Use angle facts to find out information to help you to answer the question.

⊙ Write your solution giving a reason for each step.

⊙ When you have finished, check your reasoning and make sure you have answered the question.

Example

ABC is an isosceles triangle with AB = AC.

From B, a line BP is been drawn to meet AC at right angles.

Prove that angle PBC is half angle CAB.

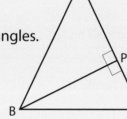

$c = 90 - b$ (angles in a triangle)

$d = 90 - a$ (angles in a triangle)

Angles ABC and ACB are equal (isosceles triangle)

$a = 180 - 2b$

$\frac{1}{2}a = 90 - b = c$

Hence $c = \frac{1}{2}a$ or $\angle PBC = \frac{1}{2}\angle CAB$

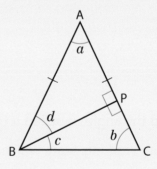

① ABC is an isosceles triangle with AB = AC.

AD is parallel to BE.

Find the values of x, y and z.

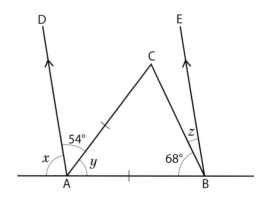

2 ABC is an isosceles triangle with AB = BC.

CBD is an isosceles triangle with BC = BD.

Prove that angle ABD is double the size of angle ACD.

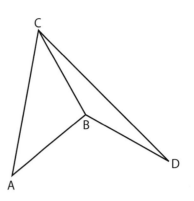

TASK 3: Solving longer problems

 Points to remember

⊙ Use information given in the question to label the diagram. Look for:
  – equal angles;
  – equal lengths.
⊙ Use the angle facts in Task 1 to find out information to help you to answer the question.

1 Copy the diagram. Find the value of x.

Hint
Label the vertices and angles in your copy of the diagram to help you to explain the steps in your reasoning.

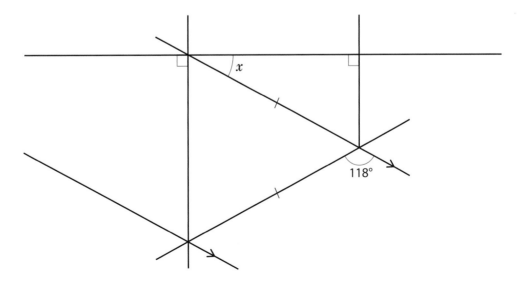

TASK 4: Drawing 3D objects

 Points to remember

- An **isometric drawing** shows an object that has been rotated and tilted.
- The **plan view** looks at the object from directly above.
- The **side and front elevations** show the object from the side and front.
- Different objects can have the same plan view, front elevation and side elevation.

Example

These drawings show the same flat-roofed house.

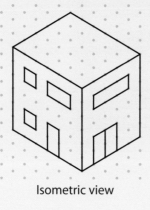

Isometric view

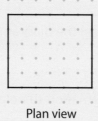

Plan view

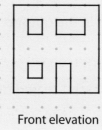

Front elevation

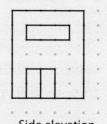

Side elevation

You will need some squared paper.

1. On squared paper, draw the plan view, side elevation and front elevation for each of these shapes.

a
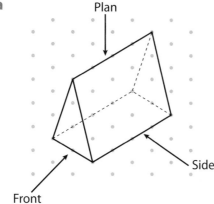

b
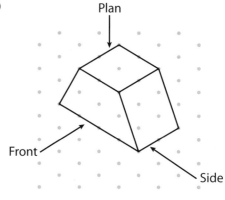

(2) Here are the front elevation and side elevation of a prism.

Front elevation

Side elevation

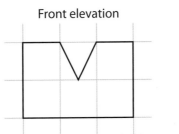
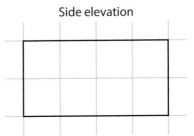

The front elevation shows the cross-section of the prism.

a On squared paper, draw a plan of the prism.　　**b** Draw a 3D sketch of the prism.

TASK 5: Drawing plans and elevations

Points to remember

⊙ An isometric drawing shows an object that has been rotated and tilted.

⊙ The plan view looks at the object from directly above.

⊙ The side and front elevations show the object from the side and front.

⊙ Different objects can have the same plan view, front elevation and side elevation.

Example

The diagrams show the set of views for a model made of four linking cubes.

Isometric view

Plan view

Side elevation

Front elevation

You will need isometric and square dotty paper, a ruler and sharp pencil.

(1) Imagine four more models made from four linking cubes. Each model should be different. For each model, draw the isometric view.

(2) For each of your four models, draw the plan view and front and side elevations.

TASK 6: More plans and elevations

Points to remember

- The plan view looks at the object from directly above.
- The side and front elevations show the object from the side and front.
- Different objects can have the same plan view, front elevation and side elevation.

1. The diagrams show the isometric view and another view for each of four different models.

   Match the diagrams to make four pairs.
   Each pair should be the isometric view and another view of the same model.

A

B

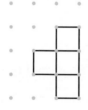

C

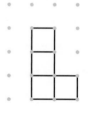

D

E

F

G

H

TASK 7: Solving problems using surface area and volume

Points to remember

⊙ Surface area is measured in square units.

⊙ To find the surface area of a cuboid, calculate the area of each of the six rectangular faces and add them together.

(1) You have 64 chips on a plate at lunchtime.

How could the chips be arranged so that they keep as warm as possible?

Use calculations to explain your answer.

For example, you could imagine that the chips are each 1 cm by 1 cm by 5 cm and that they are packed in a square 8 by 8 block one chip high.

Alternatively, you could arrange them in one long line.

TASK 8: Surface area and volume of prisms

⦿ Points to remember

⦿ A **prism** is a polyhedron with two parallel and congruent bases.
Its side faces are rectangles perpendicular to the bases.
Cross-sections parallel to a base are identical to the base.

⦿ The **surface area of a prism** is the sum of the area of each of the faces.

⦿ The **volume of a prism** is calculated by:

volume of a prism = area of base × perpendicular height

(1) Some boxes are made from rectangular sheets of card.

The card is marked with cut and fold lines as in the diagram below.
The cuts are shown as solid lines and the folds as dotted lines.

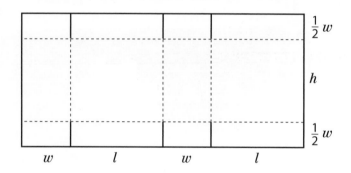 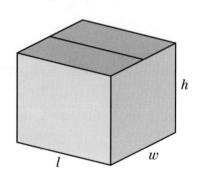

The net is used to make a box from a sheet of card 1 m long and 40 cm wide.

The box is 20 cm high.

Calculate the volume of the box. Show all your calculations.

Calculations and calculators

TASK 1: Powers of 10

> ### ⦿ Points to remember
>
> ⦿ × 0.1 is equivalent to ÷ 10.
> ⦿ × 0.01 is equivalent to ÷ 100.
> ⦿ × 0.001 is equivalent to ÷ 1000.
> ⦿ ÷ 0.1 is equivalent to × 10.
> ⦿ ÷ 0.01 is equivalent to × 100.
> ⦿ ÷ 0.001 is equivalent to × 1000.

Answer these questions **without using your calculator**.

1. Write the answers to these.

   a 8.3×10

   b 0.42×10^2

   c 6.95×10^3

   d $31 \div 10^3$

   e $417 \div 10^2$

   f $834 \div 10^3$

   g 0.006×10^2

   h $75 \div 10^2$

2. Multiply these numbers by 0.01.

   a 7.9

   b 652

   c 0.3

3. Multiply these numbers by 0.001.

   a 23.4

   b 4837

   c 0.2

4. Divide these numbers by 0.1.

   a 0.8

   b 65

   c 0.037

5. Divide these numbers by 0.001.

   a 31.7

   b 0.96

   c 0.0053

TASK 2: Rounding and approximation

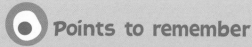

Points to remember

⊙ When you round an answer, make sure it has the required number of decimal places, e.g. 4.96 rounded to one decimal place is 5.0, not 5.

⊙ Round before a calculation to estimate the answer.

⊙ When you work out the actual answer, don't round until after you have completed the calculation.

⊙ A length in metres rounded to two decimal places is to the nearest centimetre.

① Work these out correct to the nearest penny.

   a £54.65 ÷ 4   **b** £21.99 ÷ 7   **c** £3.20 ÷ 6   **d** £283.50 ÷ 16

② A snack bar on the beach took £1407.45 for the snacks sold on a Sunday in July.

702 people bought a snack.
What was the mean amount each person spent to the nearest penny?

③ Write an estimate for the answer to each calculation.

   a 878 ÷ 28   **b** 641 × 22   **c** 83 ÷ 3.7

   d 4.95 × 5.1   **e** 7.65 ÷ 1.8   **f** 0.037 × 506

   g 0.0031 × 0.82   **h** 0.48 ÷ 0.019   **i** $(0.049)^2$

   j $\dfrac{216.7 + 3.2}{48.9 + 10.3}$ **k** $\dfrac{39 \times 68}{81}$ **l** $\dfrac{79.5 \times 23.7}{7.8 \times 6.1}$

TASK 3: Mental calculations with decimals

◉ Points to remember

⊙ Given a calculation, check first to see if you can do it mentally.

⊙ Use facts you know to work out new facts.
For example, to multiply by 5, multiply by 10, then halve.

⊙ When a is greater than 1:
  – multiplying a number by a makes it bigger;
  – dividing a number by a makes it smaller.

⊙ When a is less than 1:
  – multiplying a number by a makes it smaller;
  – dividing a number by a makes it bigger.

Do these **without using a calculator**.

1 In an arithmagon, the number in each square is the sum
of the two numbers on either side of it.

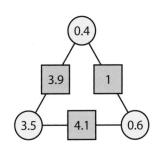

Copy and complete these arithmagons.

a

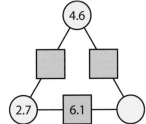

b

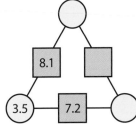

c

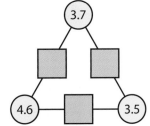

d

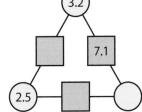

2 This is a multiplication table.

Each number is the product of the number at the beginning of the row and the number at the top of the column.

×	3	0.06	1.2
0.2	0.6	0.012	0.24
1.5	4.5	0.09	1.8

For example, 4.5 is the product of 1.5 × 3.

Copy and complete this multiplication table.

×	0.3		10
			1
2.5		0.05	
	0.15		

TASK 4: Written calculations with decimals

Points to remember

- For written calculations with decimals:
  - estimate the answer;
  - choose an efficient method;
  - use the estimate to check the size of the answer and to make sure that any decimal point is in the right place.
- You can also check answers by using inverse operations.

Do these questions **without using a calculator**. Show your working.

1 Work out:

a 38.4 + 14.19   b 21.4 − 7.28   c 4.9 × 6.5

d 5.06 × 0.3   e 8.45 ÷ 0.5   f 6.72 ÷ 1.6

2 a A jug with water in it weighs 1.32 kg.
The jug alone weighs 275 g.
What is the mass of the water in the jug in kilograms?

b The jug held 2 litres of water when it was full.
There is now 913 ml of water in the jug.
How many litres of water have been used?

3 An isosceles triangle has two equal sides of 2.55 cm and a base of 2.4 cm.
Its height is 2.25 cm.

    a What is the perimeter of the triangle in centimetres?

    b What is the area of the triangle in square centimetres?

TASK 5: Using a calculator

◉ Points to remember

When you use a calculator:

- ⊙ estimate the result of a calculation;
- ⊙ clear all before each new calculation;
- ⊙ use the clear key to clear the last entry;
- ⊙ use the memory to store parts of a calculation or to keep a total;
- ⊙ check the answer against the estimate;
- ⊙ if appropriate, round answers to a suitable number of decimal places.

Use your calculator for these questions.

1 Work out the value of each expression.
Put brackets in where necessary.
Give your answers correct to two decimal places.

    a $\dfrac{13.6 - 4.51}{3.72 + 6.3}$
    b $\dfrac{3.6 \times 5.7}{\sqrt{21}}$
    c $\dfrac{(6.1 - 2.7)^2}{5.3}$

    d $\frac{1}{2}\sqrt{16^2 + 23^2}$
    e $\dfrac{\sqrt{14.6 - 3.29}}{8}$
    f $\sqrt{\dfrac{17 + 25}{6}}$

2 Investigate.

    Each ✶ represents a missing sign ($+$, $-$, $\times$ or $\div$).

    Copy and complete the calculations.

    a $(3.6 \ast 1.6) \ast 0.52 = 1.17$

    b $4.3 \ast (1.7 \ast 0.8) = 4.78$

TASK 6: Problems involving measures

① A shopping basket contains:

1.15 kg	cabbage
1.6 kg	corn oil
454 g	marmalade
87 g	lemon
1.3 kg	oranges
340 g	coffee

What is the total mass of the goods in the basket?

② A water container contains 25 litres of water.
These amounts of water are drawn off:

2.35 litres, 1.06 litres, 940 millilitres, 3.8 litres

How much water is left in the container?

③ The diagram shows the cross-section of a plastic hosepipe.
The external diameter is 1.7 cm.
The internal diameter is 14 mm.

Find the area of the plastic in the cross-section:

a in square centimetres

b in square millimetres

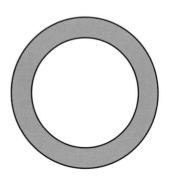

④ Calculate these areas in square centimetres.
Give each answer correct to one decimal place.

a a parallelogram

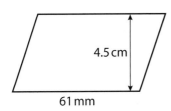

4.5 cm

61 mm

b a trapezium

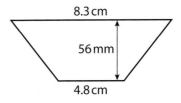

8.3 cm

56 mm

4.8 cm

⑤ The diagram shows the measurements of a prism.

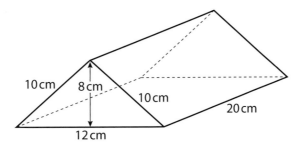

10 cm   8 cm   10 cm   20 cm

12 cm

Calculate the total surface area of the prism.

Probability 1

TASK 1: Simple probability

⊙ Points to remember

- For equally likely outcomes, the **theoretical probability** of an event is:

$$\frac{\text{number of successful outcomes}}{\text{total number of possible outcomes}}$$

You will need compasses, ruler, protractor and coloured pencils.

1. Design a spinner where the probability of getting blue is double that of getting yellow.

2. Design a different spinner where the probability of getting blue is still double that of getting yellow.

3. Design a spinner where the probability of getting red is double that of getting green and the probability of getting green is double that of getting black.

4. Design a spinner of your own and write down three things about the probabilities of the different colours.

TASK 2: Equally likely outcomes with two events

⊙ Points to remember

- When two events occur at the same time or one after the other, you can use a table to show the equally likely outcomes.
- This type of table is called a **sample space diagram**.

1. Emil has two spinners.
   One has four sections labelled 1, 2, 3 and 4.
   The other has five sections labelled 5, 6, 7, 8 and 9.

   a. Make a table to show all the equally likely outcomes from spinning the two spinners and adding the scores.

   b. Which outcome is the least likely?

   c. Which outcome is the most likely?

   d. Write down two outcomes that have the same probability.

2. a. Choose another rule for scoring with the spinners.
      Complete another table for your rule.

   b. Write down three statements about the probabilities using your table.

TASK 3: Mutually exclusive events

Points to remember

- Outcomes that cannot occur at the same time are **mutually exclusive**.
- The sum of the probabilities of all the mutually exclusive outcomes of an experiment is 1.
- If the probability of an event occurring is p, then the probability of it not occurring is $1 - p$.
- If A and B are mutually exclusive events then:

   probability of A or B = probability of A + probability of B

1. What are the possible outcomes when you spin one coin?

2. What are the possible outcomes when you spin 2 coins?

3. What are the possible outcomes when you spin 3 coins?

   It might help to list all the outcomes systematically.

4. Can you see a pattern? Describe it.

   Use the pattern to predict the number of possible outcomes for 4 coins and then 5 coins.

TASK 4: Practical probability experiments

> ### ● Points to remember
>
> ⊙ For equally likely outcomes, the **theoretical probability** of an event is:
>
> $$\frac{\text{number of successful outcomes}}{\text{total number of possible outcomes}}$$
>
> ⊙ The **experimental probability** of an event is:
>
> $$\frac{\text{number of successful trials}}{\text{total number of trials}}$$
>
> ⊙ As you do more and more trials, the experimental probability becomes closer in value to theoretical probability.

You will need a piece of paper and some scissors.

① Design your own probability experiment.

> ⊡ Cut 12 equal 'cards' from your piece of paper.
> ⊡ Choose three to five different simple symbols, such as a shape or a letter.
>
>
>
> ⊡ Label each of your 12 cards with one of your three to five symbols.
>   You will need to use at least some of the symbols more than once.
>   Try to use each symbol a different number of times.
> ⊡ Shuffle the cards and place them face down.
> ⊡ Prepare a tally chart to record how many times you pick each symbol.
> ⊡ Now pick a card at random and record the symbol in the tally chart.
>   Put the card back face down, and shuffle the cards again.
> ⊡ Repeat this 20 times.

② Calculate the experimental probability of getting each symbol.

③ Turn your cards over. Calculate the theoretical probability of getting each symbol.

④ Write a sentence comparing the two sets of probabilities.

TASK 5: Simulating probability experiments

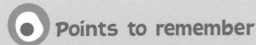

Points to remember

⊙ A **simulation** is an easy-to-do experiment that behaves in the same way as the original experiment.

⊙ A **random number generator** can simulate situations more quickly than carrying out an actual experiment.

⊙ Repeated experiments may give different outcomes.

Simulating spinning a spinner

1 This list has 30 random numbers which were generated by using a calculator.

32	15	21	20	37	16	7	18	40	10
20	3	39	13	21	17	10	5	39	9
7	38	16	25	9	23	11	30	15	17

a Make the random numbers represent these outcomes:

Numbers 1–10 = green
Numbers 11–20 = red
Numbers 21–30 = blue
Numbers 31–40 = yellow

Count up the number of times each colour is spun.

b Calculate the experimental probability of getting each colour using the random number simulation.

2 The table shows the set of results for the same simulation repeated for another set of random numbers.

Outcome	Frequency
Green	6
Red	6
Blue	7
Yellow	11

Calculate the experimental probability of getting each colour using the frequencies in the table.

3 Combine the two sets of results from questions **1** and **2**.

Use the new set of results to calculate the experimental probability of getting each colour.

TASK 1: Generating linear graphs using ICT

Points to remember

⊙ The equation of a linear graph is usually written in the form $y = ax + b$.

⊙ What you do to one side of an equation you must do to the other side.

⊙ You can divide each term in an equation by the same number.

1 Rearrange these equations in the form $y = ax + b$.

   a $y - 5x + 7 = 0$ **b** $y - 4x = 1$

   c $x - y = 6$ **d** $y - 8x = -3$

   e $2y + 4x - 6 = 0$ **f** $3y - 9x + 30 = 0$

2 Look again at the equations in question 1.
Write the gradient and intercept on the y-axis for each of the graphs of the equations.

TASK 2: Sketching graphs

Points to remember

⊙ When a linear equation is in the form $y = ax + b$:

  – a, the coefficient of x, is the **gradient** of the graph;

  – b is the **intercept** on the y-axis.

⊙ When the line $y = 2x + 3$ is **translated** 4 units up,
the equation of the new line is $y = 2x + 7$.
The gradient of the line does not change.

⊙ When the line $y = 2x + 3$ is **reflected** in the y-axis,
the equation of the new line is $y = -2x + 3$.

⊙ When the line $y = 2x + 3$ is reflected in the x-axis,
the equation of the new line is $y = -2x - 3$.

You will need squared paper.

1. a On squared paper, sketch the graph of $y = 3x - 2$ on a blank set of axes.
   b On the same axes, sketch the graph when $y = 3x - 2$ has been translated by 3 units up.
   c Write the equation of the graph you have sketched.

2. a On squared paper, sketch the graph of $y = x + 5$ on a blank set of axes.
   b On the same axes, sketch the graph when $y = x + 5$ has been reflected in the y-axis.
   c Write the equation of the graph you have just sketched.

TASK 3: Drawing accurate graphs

⦿ Points to remember

- For **any** value of x in an equation such as $y = 3x + 2$, you can find a value of y.
- To draw an accurate straight-line graph, you need the coordinates of three points: two to define the line and the third to check your accuracy.

You will need graph paper.

1. Copy and complete these tables.

a
x	−2	0	2
$y = 2x + 1$			

b
x	−1	0	1
$y = 3x - 2$			

c
x	0	1	2
$y = -x + 1$			

Now use graph paper, pencil and ruler to draw an accurate graph of each equation in the tables.

Draw each graph on a new grid.

Remember to continue the line to the edge of the grid.

TASK 4: Direct proportion

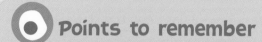

Points to remember

- When y is **directly proportional** to x you write $y \propto x$, giving the equation $y = kx$.
- The graph of $y = kx$ is a straight line passing through the origin with gradient k.

1. Dominic looked up the exchange rate for pounds to euros on the Internet.

   He found this graph and used it to make some estimates.

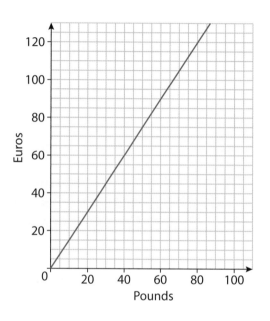

   a Estimate how many euros he will get for £50.

   b Estimate how many euros he will get for £300.

   c Estimate the cost of a £25 shirt in euros.

   d Estimate the cost in pounds of a train journey costing 60 euros.

   e Dominic pays 50 euros for a meal.
   Estimate how much this is in pounds.

   f Dominic returns from a holiday in France with 80 euros.
   About how many pounds is this?

2. These tables represent directly proportional relationships $y \propto x$ or $y = kx$.
Work out the value of k in each case.

a

x	0	1	2
y	0	7	14

b

x	3	5	7
y	4.5	7.5	10.5

c

x	−1	0	1
y	−8	0	8

d

x	−2	0	2
y	4	0	−4

TASK 5: Reflecting graphs in $y = x$

> ### ● Points to remember
>
> ⊙ When the point (a, b) is reflected in the line $y = x$,
>   the image is the point (b, a).
> ⊙ When the line with equation $y = ax + b$ is reflected in the line $y = x$,
>   the equation of the image line is $x = ay + b$.

1. a Write the equation of the blue line.

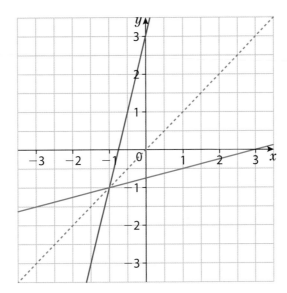

   b The pink line is the reflection of the blue line in the dotted line $y = x$.
      Write the equation of the pink line.

   c Write what you notice about the two equations.

TASK 6: Simple quadratic graphs using ICT

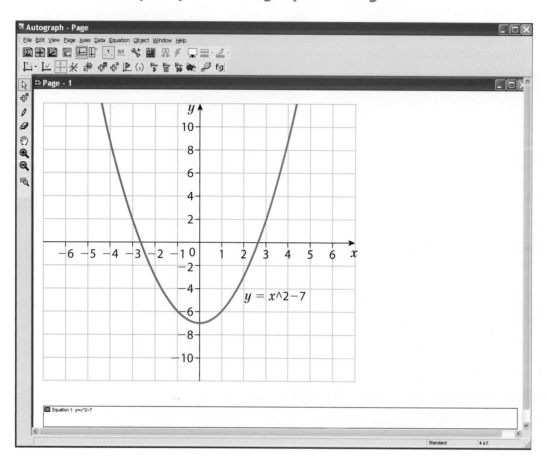

Points to remember

- **Quadratic graphs** are always U-shaped.
- Quadratic graphs do not always cut the x-axis.

You will need squared paper.

1. a On squared paper, sketch the graph of $y = x^2$ on a blank set of axes.

   b On the same set of axes, sketch the graphs of:
   $$y = x^2 + 1, y = x^2 + 3, y = x^2 - 1, y = x^2 - 4$$

2. a On squared paper, sketch the graph of $y = x^2$ on a blank set of axes.

   b On the same set of axes, sketch the graphs of:
   $$y = 2x^2, y = 3x^2, y = 4x^2, y = 0.5x^2$$

Transformations

TASK 1: Planes of symmetry

 Points to remember

⊙ A plane of symmetry divides a 3D shape into two equal halves that are mirror images of each other.

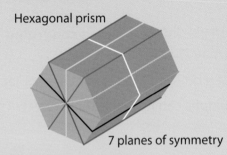

Hexagonal prism

7 planes of symmetry

⊙ The number of **planes of symmetry** in a right prism is one more than the number of lines of symmetry of the cross-section.

⊙ A cube has 9 planes of symmetry.

⊙ A right pyramid has the same number of planes of symmetry as lines of symmetry of the base.

1 Write the number of planes of symmetry in each of these 3D shapes.

a

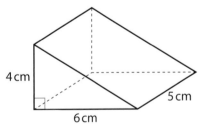

2 cm

8 cm

5 cm

b

4 cm

5 cm

6 cm

c

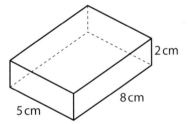

5 cm

5 cm 4 cm

8 cm

6 cm

d

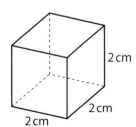

2 cm

2 cm

2 cm

2 A right pyramid has a base that is a regular pentagon.
   How many planes of symmetry does the pyramid have?

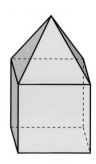

3 The picture shows a square-based
   pyramid on top of a cube.

   The square faces are the same size.

   How many planes of symmetry does the shape have?

TASK 2: Combined transformations

You will need squared paper.

1 Copy the diagram on squared paper.

   Rotate the rectangle 180° clockwise
   about the origin (0, 0).

   What single transformation would have
   the same effect?

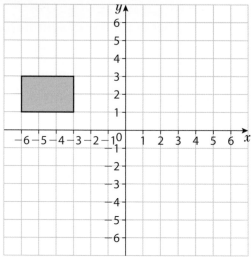

2 Copy this diagram on squared paper.

   Image 1 is the reflection of the object in a
   mirror line. Draw the mirror line.

   Image 2 is the reflection of image 1 in a
   mirror line. Draw the mirror line.

   Describe a single transformation to transform
   the object to image 2.

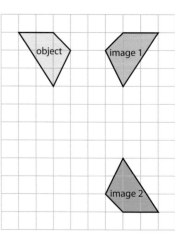

3 Describe a single transformation that would transform the object to the image.

Now describe a different way to transform the object to the image using more than one transformation.

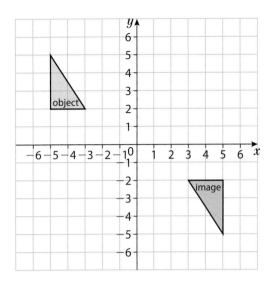

TASK 3: Islamic patterns

Points to remember

⊙ Islamic patterns are often based on tiles that have four lines of symmetry and rotation symmetry of order 4.

Did you know that...?

Islamic patterns involve repeated translations, rotations and reflections.

They are seen in many buildings and on pieces of furniture.

The patterns are often created around a single tile that is repeated many times to form the pattern.

Here is a single tile.

Each tile has four lines of symmetry and order of rotation 4.

When the tile is translated it creates this pattern.

1 Look at the shapes in this tiling pattern.

a How many lines of symmetry are there?

b What is the order of rotation symmetry?

c Describe two different ways to transform the blue triangle in the top left corner onto the blue triangle in the top right corner.

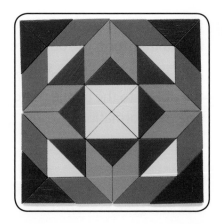

2 Often the starting pattern for a pattern is a tile that has four lines of symmetry and rotation symmetry of order 4.

Draw a 5 cm square. Design your own tile that has four lines of symmetry and rotation symmetry of order 4.

TASK 4: Enlargements

Points to remember

- **Scale factor** $= \dfrac{\text{length of side of image}}{\text{length of corresponding side of object}}$

- Lines joining corresponding points of the object and image meet at the **centre of enlargement**.

- If O is the centre of enlargement, then for corresponding points A and A' on the object and image:

  OA' = scale factor × OA

You will need squared paper.

1 Copy this diagram on squared paper.

Enlarge the shape by a scale factor of 3 with a centre of enlargement (3, 7).

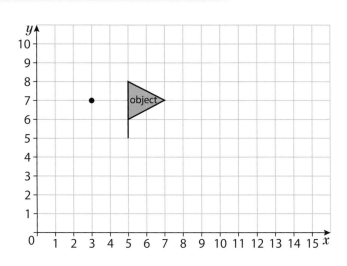

2 Copy this diagram on squared paper.

Enlarge the shape by a scale factor of 4 with a centre of enlargement at (3, 12).

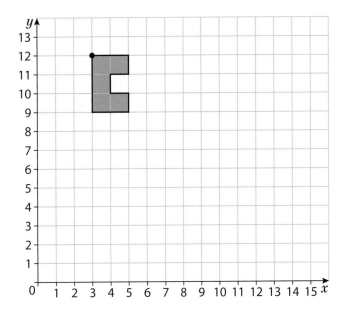

3 Look at this diagram.
The image is an enlargement of the object.

a What is the scale factor of enlargement?

b What are the coordinates of the centre of enlargement?

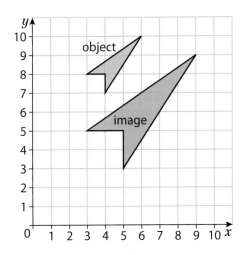

TASK 5: Enlargements in real-life applications

Points to remember

- Scale factor = $\dfrac{\text{length of side of image}}{\text{length of corresponding side of object}}$

- A scale of 1 cm to 4 m means that every 1 cm of the model or map represents 4 m of the real object.

- A scale of 1 cm to 4 m can also be written as 1 : 400.

1. In each pair of shapes, the bigger shape is an enlargement of the smaller shape. Work out the length of the missing side.

a

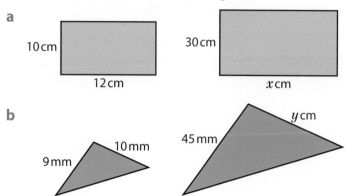

10 cm
12 cm

30 cm
x cm

b

9 mm
10 mm

45 mm
y cm

2. George has a picture of his dog.

He decides to enlarge the picture using a scale factor of 2.

What are the dimensions of the enlarged picture?

4 cm

6 cm

3. A model plane has a scale of 1 to 250. The model is 8 cm long.
How long is the real plane?

4. The scale on a map is 1 cm to 8 km. Two points are 9.4 cm apart on the map.
How many kilometres is that?

5. Coniston Water is 8 km long.
On a map it measures 16 cm.
What is the scale of the map?

TASK 6: Length, area and volume

1. a A rectangle has dimensions 6 cm by 7 cm.
      Work out the perimeter and area of the rectangle.

   b The sides of the rectangle are enlarged by a scale factor of 3.
      Work out the perimeter and area of the enlarged rectangle.

   c How many times bigger is the area of the enlarged rectangle
      than the area of the original rectangle?

2. A cuboid has dimensions 4 cm by 5 cm by 7 cm.

   a What is the volume of the cuboid?

   b The sides of the cuboid are enlarged by a scale factor of 4.
      What is the volume of the enlarged cuboid?

   c How many times bigger is the volume of the enlarged cuboid
      than the volume of the original cuboid?

3. On a plan of a new house the scale is 1 cm to 5 m.

   a The garden on the plan is a rectangle 4 cm by 6 cm.
      What is the area of the real garden?

   b A fencing panel is 2 metres long and costs £8.50.
      What is the cost of fencing the two longer sides and one short side of the garden?

4. The distance between two towns is 6 km.
   On a map, the distance between the towns is 30 cm.
   Write the scale of the map as a ratio.

5. A cuboid has a total surface area of 12 cm².
   The cuboid is enlarged so that each side is twice as long.
   What is the total surface area of the enlarged cuboid?

Using algebra

TASK 1: Using graphs to solve problems

> ### ⊙ Points to remember
>
> ⊙ You can explore many mathematical problems by using algebra.
>
> ⊙ For example, you may be able to set up an equation and draw a graph.
>
> ⊙ Put values that you estimate from a graph back into the original equation to check them.

1 The table shows the values of x and y, where y is proportional to x.

x	3	6	P
y	7	Q	35

What are the values of P and Q?

2 The time, T seconds, taken for a kettle to boil is directly proportional to the amount, A litres, of water in the kettle.

When $A = 2$, $T = 100$.

  a Write a formula for T in terms of A.

  b Find the value of T when $A = 3$.

  c The kettle takes 3 minutes to boil.
    How much water is in it?

3 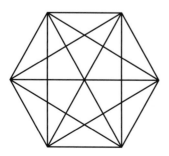 The perimeter, P cm, of a regular hexagon is proportional to the length, l cm, of its longest diagonal.

When $l = 5$, $P = 15$.

  a Write a formula for P in terms of l.

  b The value of l increases from 7 to 9.
    Find the increase in the value of P.

TASK 2: Using algebra in geometry problems

1 **a** The height of the triangle is $4x$.
The base is $x + 6$.
Show that the formula for the area of the triangle is $2x^2 + 12x$.

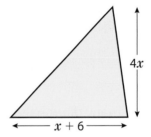

b This is the graph of $y = 2x^2 + 12x$.

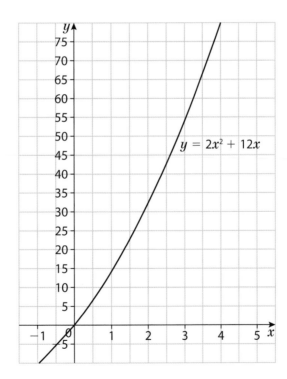

Estimate the value of x when the the area of the triangle is 70 cm².

c Use trial and improvement to find the value of x to two decimal places.

TASK 3: Using algebra in investigations

Points to remember

⊙ When you start an investigation, break the problem down into smaller parts.

⊙ Work systematically and record your results in a table as you go along.

⊙ Look for patterns.

⊙ Make a conjecture and test it.

⊙ See if you can make a generalisation.

⊙ Check that you have answered the question and ask yourself further questions.

1   a   How many diagonals has a square?

    b   How many diagonals are there in this pentagon?

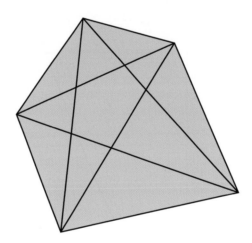

    c   How many diagonals are there in a hexagon?

    d   Look for a pattern by checking further polygons.

    e   Find a formula for the number of diagonals in an n-sided polygon.

Enquiry 2

TASK 1: Calculating statistics

 Points to remember

- The **range** is the difference between the smallest value in the data set and the largest.
- The **median** is the middle value when the values in the data set are listed in order of size. It is less affected by extreme values than the mean.
- The **mode** is the value in the data set that appears most often. It is affected by how often values are repeated, not by the values themselves.
- The **mean** is the sum of all the values in the data set divided by the number of values. It gives an indication of all the values but it is more affected by extreme values than either the median or the mode.

Example

The frequency table shows the shoe sizes of 50 pupils. Find the mean of the data in the table.

Value	Frequency
4	12
5	11
6	9
7	15
8	3

The total of the shoe sizes is:

$(12 \times 4) + (11 \times 5) + (9 \times 6) + (15 \times 7) + (3 \times 8)$

$= 286$

The mean is $286 \div 50 = 5.72$.

You may **use a calculator** for this task.

1. The table shows 50 children's weekly pocket money.
   a What is the range of the amount of pocket money received by the children?
   b What is the mode?
   c What is the median?
   d What is the mean?
   e Which of the mean, median and mode gives the best indication of the average pocket money?

Amount of pocket money	Frequency
£1.00	8
£1.20	9
£1.50	11
£2.00	10
£2.50	12

2 The table shows the marks for 100 pupils in a mental maths test.

- **a** What is the range of the marks in the test?
- **b** What is the mode?
- **c** What is the median?
- **d** What is the mean?
- **e** Which of the mean, median and mode gives the best indication of the average mark?

Test mark	Frequency
3	3
4	5
5	8
6	15
7	21
8	33
9	12
10	3

TASK 2: Line graphs for time series

 Points to remember

- ⊙ **Line graphs** are useful for looking at how data changes over time.
- ⊙ Time always goes on the horizontal axis.
- ⊙ Displaying related line graphs on the same axes helps you to compare data.

Example

Draw a line graph for this table.

Year	1960	1970	1980	1990	2000
Number of TV sets per 1000	229.1	323.6	401.2	432.6	891.8

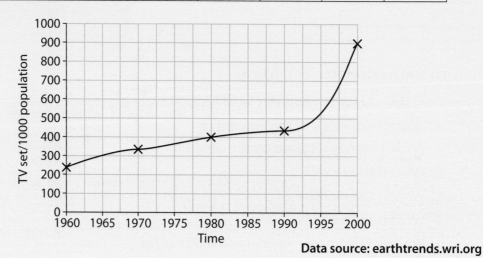

Data source: earthtrends.wri.org

You will need graph paper, a sharp pencil and a ruler.

1 The table shows the number of television sets per 1000 population in two countries.

	1970	1980	1990	2000	2004
Egypt	15	32	117	227	250
South Korea	19	165	207	414	477

Data source: earthtrends.wri.org

a Draw a line graph to illustrate the data.
Use one line for Egypt and one line for South Korea.
Use the paper in landscape format.
Put years on the horizontal axis. Use 5 cm for every 10 years.
Use 2 cm for 100 TV sets on the vertical axis.

b Write sentences to say what the graph shows about:
 ◉ the change in television set ownership over time;
 ◉ the differences in television set ownership between the two countries.

TASK 3: Scatter graphs

◉ Points to remember

◉ **Scatter graphs** are useful for looking for connections between quantities.

◉ A **positive correlation** is when one variable increases as the other increases. A **negative correlation** is when one variable decreases as the other increases.

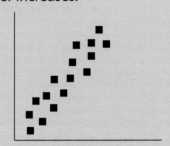
Strong positive correlation

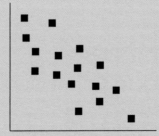
Weak negative correlation

◉ When points are grouped closely the correlation is **strong**. When points are more spread out the correlation is **weak**.

◉ When the points are all spread out this indicates that there is **no correlation** between the variables.

For each question write down the type of correlation.

Then write a sentence describing the relationship between the two variables.

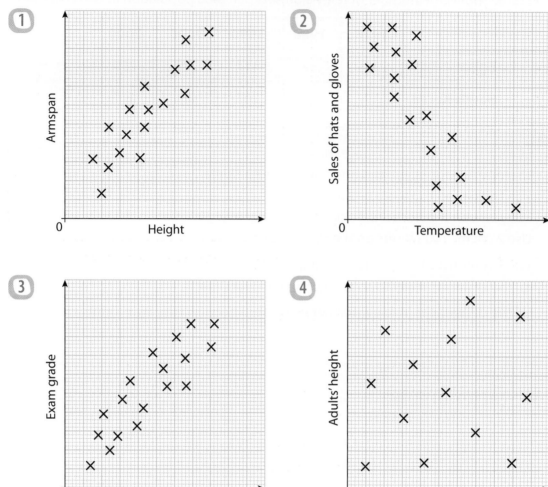

TASK 4: Collecting and organising data

⊙ Points to remember

A questionnaire for a survey needs to have questions that:

⊙ are clear and unambiguous;

⊙ have a good set of options for people to choose from;

⊙ are relevant to the purpose of the survey.

Plastic for recycling

Recycling symbol on plastic wrapper

 ① This is an example of a questionnaire about recycling.

> **1** Do you recycle?
>
> **2** How often?
>
> **3** What items do you recycle?
>
> **4** Do you turn the lights off when you leave a room?
>
> **5** How much of your waste do you recycle?
>
> **6** Do you think it should be easier to recycle?

Look at the questionnaire.
Use the checklist below to improve it if you can.

▶ Are the questions clear and specific?

▶ Do they have a good set of options for people to choose from?

▶ Are they relevant to the purpose of the survey?

② Write a questionnaire with at least six questions to find out about people's views on recycling.

Remember to:

▶ only ask relevant questions;

▶ give people a good range of options for the questions;

▶ make your questions clear;

▶ think about who might be answering the questions.

TASK 5: Analysing and representing data

◉ Points to remember

⊙ Different charts and diagrams are good for showing different kinds of data and different features of that data.

⊙ Choose a chart or diagram that helps you to answer your question and explain why you chose it.

⊙ You can use spreadsheet software to produce graphs and charts of tables of data.

Recycling collection point, North London

Sellafield Nuclear Reprocessing Plant, England

You will need some graph paper.

① This table shows amounts of recycling in England in 2003–04.

Waste type	Thousands of tonnes
Paper and card	1271
Glass	568
Compost	1360
Scrap metal/white goods	464
Textiles, cans and plastics	118
Other	735
Total	4516

Data source: www.defra.gov.uk

a Represent the data in a graph or chart. Do it in two different ways. If you have spreadsheet software at home, you may use it.

b Which graph or chart is more informative? Explain why.

TASK 6: Interpreting data

Paper and cardboard boxes at a recycling plant in Norfolk, England

Fruit and vegetable peelings for composting in Berkshire, England

The data source for graphs in this task is www.planetark.com.

1   The graph shows the percentage of paper and cardboard recycled in 11 different industrialised countries.

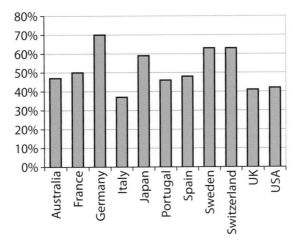

a   Write two sentences to say what the graph shows.

b   Write a sentence comparing the recycling rate in the best country compared to the worst.

2. The graph shows the percentage of glass recycled in 11 different industrialised countries.

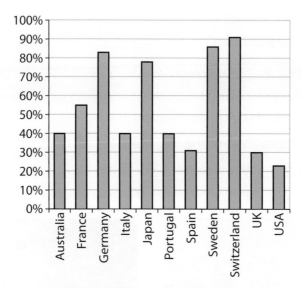

a Write two sentences to say what the graph shows.

b Pick any two countries and compare their recycling rates.

3. The graph shows the percentage of steel cans recycled in 11 different industrialised countries.

Write two sentences to say what the graph shows.

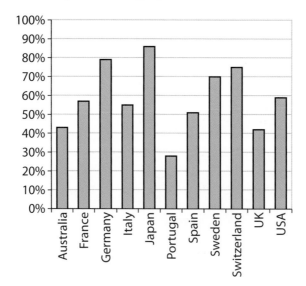

4. Pick any country and write a sentence about its recycling rate for paper and cardboard, glass and steel cans by comparing its performance in all three graphs.

TASK 7: Reporting and evaluating

 Points to remember

When you finish a statistical project, evaluate your results:

⊙ make sure that you have answered the original question;

⊙ give a conclusion by summarising what you have found out;

⊙ consider whether there are further questions you could ask;

⊙ consider how you could improve your work next time.

Key features of a graph include:

⊙ the general shape;

⊙ the greatest and least values;

⊙ any points where the shape changes.

Example

What conclusion can you draw from this graph?

The bar graph shows that most people found it easy or very easy to recycle their rubbish.

A few people found it difficult to recycle their rubbish.

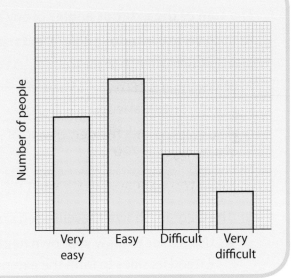

You will need a ruler, compasses and sharp pencil.

For each question sketch a graph that fits the interpretation.

1. The scatter graph shows that there is no relationship between age and commitment to recycling.

2. The pie chart shows that more than half the rubbish recycled is paper and cardboard.

   Approximately 25% is garden waste and the rest is split roughly equally between textiles, glass and plastics.

3. The line graph shows that twice as many people recycled paper and card in 2005 compared with 1995.

   The number of people recycling paper and card generally increased, although it dropped slightly in 2000 and 2001.

Angles and constructions

TASK 1: Angles in polygons

> ### ⦿ Points to remember
>
> ⊙ A **polygon** is a 2D shape with three or more straight sides.
> The number of sides equals the number of vertices.
> ⊙ The **sum of the exterior angles** of any polygon is **360°**.
> ⊙ At each vertex: **interior angle + exterior angle = 180°**.
> ⊙ The sum of the interior angles:
> – of a triangle is 180°;
> – of a quadrilateral is 360°;
> – of a pentagon is 540°;
> – of a hexagon is **720°**.

1   The diagram shows a seven-sided polygon, a heptagon.

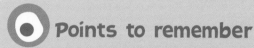

   a   Use a ruler to draw your own heptagon.
        Extend its sides to form the exterior angles.
        Label the interior angles *I* and the exterior angles *E*.

   b   What is the sum of the interior and exterior angles
        at each vertex?

   c   Write down the number of vertices, n.
        Work out the sum of all the interior and exterior angles.

   d   What is the sum of the exterior angles of a heptagon? Explain your answer.

   e   Use your answer to parts **c** and **d** to work out the sum of the interior angles of a
        heptagon.

2   a   Draw another heptagon. Draw all possible diagonals from one vertex.

   b   How many diagonals have you drawn?

   c   How many triangles do the diagonals make inside the heptagon?

   d   Use your answer to part **c** to work out the sum of the interior angles of a heptagon.

   e   Check that your answer to part **d** agrees with your answer to question **1** part **e**.

TASK 2: Regular polygons

Points to remember

⊙ The sum of the exterior angles of any polygon is 360°.

⊙ A regular polygon has equal sides and equal angles.

⊙ The exterior angle of a regular polygon with n sides is $360 \div n$.

⊙ The Logo procedure for drawing an n-sided regular polygon is:

```
TO POLYGON :n
    REPEAT :n [FD 100 RT 360/:n]
END
```

1. Work out the exterior angle of each of these regular polygons.

   a   **b**    **c**

2. A nonagon is a 9-sided polygon.
   Write a Logo procedure to draw a regular nonagon.

3. A dodecagon is a 12-sided polygon.

   Sam types this Logo procedure for a regular dodecagon into his computer.

   ```
   TO DODECAGON
       REPEAT 12 [FD 100 RT 36]
   END
   ```

   Sam looks at the shape that appears on the computer screen. He realises that he has made a mistake.

   a Describe what Sam sees on his computer screen.

   b Identify Sam's mistake and write a correct Logo procedure for a regular dodecagon.

4. The exterior angle of a regular polygon is 10°.
   Write a Logo procedure to draw this regular polygon.

TASK 3: Regular polygons and the circle

⦿ Points to remember

⊙ The vertices of a regular polygon lie on the circumference of a circle.

⊙ Lines joining the centre of a regular n-sided polygon to each vertex divide the regular polygon into n equal-sized isosceles triangles.

⊙ Each angle at the centre of an n-sided regular polygon is equal to $360 \div n$, the exterior angle of the polygon.

① Use compasses and a sharp pencil to draw a circle.

Use your ruler to draw on the circle a radius, a diameter and a chord.

② The diagram shows a regular dodecagon.
A circle has been drawn through each vertex.

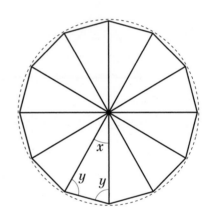

   a How many equal-sized isosceles triangles are formed by the radii?

   b Work out angles x and y.

   c Use angle y to calculate the interior angle of the regular dodecagon.

③ **a** Work out the exterior angle of a regular dodecagon.

   b Compare this with angle x.

     What do you notice?
     Explain your answer.

   c Use the exterior angle to work out the interior angle.

④ Compare your answers to question **2** part **c** and question **3** part **c**.

⑤ The angle at the centre of a regular polygon is 10°.

   a What is the exterior angle of the regular polygon?

   b What is the interior angle of the regular polygon?

   c How many sides has the polygon?

TASK 4: Angle problems and polygons

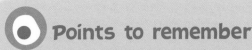

Points to remember

⊙ When you solve problems involving polygons, use these facts:
  - the sum of the interior angles of the polygon;
  - the sum of the exterior angles of a polygon is 360°;
  - the sum of the interior and exterior angles is 180°.

⊙ Given an *n*-sided regular polygon, use these facts:
  - exterior angles are equal to 360 ÷ *n*;
  - interior angles are equal to 180 − (360 ÷ *n*);
  - the angles at the centre are equal to 360 ÷ *n*.

⊙ You may be able to use the properties of isosceles triangles.

---

1 ABCDE and ABCDF are pentagons.
   ABF is an isosceles triangle.
   DFE is a right-angled triangle.
   BCDF is a quadrilateral.

   Jessica has worked out all of the angles in
   the diagram, but she has made one mistake.

   a Check the angles for all of the polygons in
      the diagram. Identify which angle is wrong.

   b Correct the mistake.

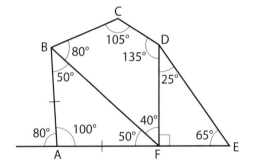

2 The diagram shows a regular hexagon
   and a regular pentagon.

   Make a sketch of the diagram.

   Work out all the unmarked angles in the diagram.
   Write them on your sketch.

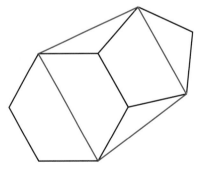

TASK 5: Polygons and parallel lines

 Points to remember

⊙ When a transversal cuts parallel lines, **corresponding** and **alternate** angles are formed.

Corresponding angles   Alternate angles

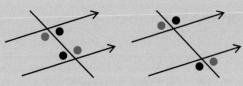

⊙ When n is even, opposite sides of a regular n-sided polygon are parallel.

⊙ Alternate and corresponding angles help to solve problems involving regular polygons.

① Work out the size of angle x.

Explain your answer, giving reasons.

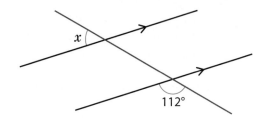

② Work out the size of angles y and z.

Explain your answer, giving reasons.

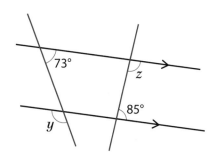

③ ABCDEFGH is a regular octagon.

  a Prove that angles x and y are equal.

  b What does this tell you about the lines AC and HD?

    Give a reason for your answer.

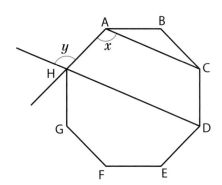

TASK 6: Constructions

Points to remember

- Standard constructions are done using only compasses and a straight edge. Always use a sharp pencil.
- Equal lengths are constructed by using compasses to draw arcs with the same radius.
- Constructions of the perpendicular bisector of a line segment and an angle bisector are based on the properties of the rhombus.
- To draw a regular polygon with n sides divide a circle into equal sectors. Each angle at the centre is $360 \div n$ and is measured with a protractor.

You will need compasses, ruler, protractor and a sharp pencil.

Use plain paper. Show all your construction lines.

① Follow the instructions given below to construct an **equilateral triangle**. The construction is based on methods used by the ancient Greeks.

In the diagram the construction arcs are not shown. The red lines are construction lines.

Make your construction lines as faint as possible.
- Draw a circle centre O (make the radius about 4 cm).
- Draw a diameter and label it AB.
- Construct the perpendicular bisector CD of AB.
- Construct the perpendicular bisector EF of OC to cross the circumference of the circle at E and F.
- Draw the equilateral triangle DEF.

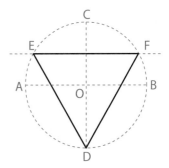

② a Construct a regular hexagon inside a circle of radius 5 cm.

  b Construct a regular nonagon.

TASK 7: Constructing triangles

Points to remember

- You can construct a triangle if you are given any of these sets of three facts: SSS, SAS, ASA, RHS.
- To construct a triangle given RHS, the perpendicular from a point on a line has to be constructed.
- To construct a line parallel to a given line AB:
  - construct perpendiculars at points A and B;
  - construct arcs of the same length with centres A and B to cut the perpendiculars at C and D;
  - join CD and extend if necessary.

You will need compasses, ruler, protractor and a sharp pencil.
Use plain paper. Show all your construction lines.

1. Construct these triangles accurately.
   All lengths are in centimetres.

   a
   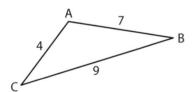

   b
   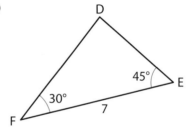

   Measure the interior angles at vertex B.

   Measure the length of ED.

2. Make accurate constructions of these right-angled triangles.

   a
   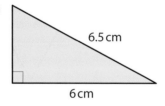

   b
   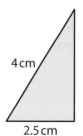

   Measure the unmarked length in each triangle.

(3) Construct this quadrilateral.

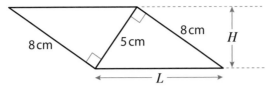

Measure the length L and perpendicular height H.

TASK 8: Loci

Points to remember

⊙ A **locus** is the path of a point that moves according to a rule.

⊙ The plural of locus is **loci**.

Use plain paper.
You will need compasses to draw arcs and circles, a ruler and a sharp pencil.

Show all your construction lines.

(1) Draw a circle with centre O and radius 4 cm.

Draw the locus of points that are exactly 6 cm from O.

Shade the region of points that are more than 4 cm from O and less than 6 cm from O.

(2) Mark two points A and B where AB = 6 cm.

Draw the locus of the set of points that are 5 cm from A.

Draw the locus of the set of points that are 4 cm from B.

Shade the region of points that are less than 5 cm from A and less than 4 cm from B.

(3) Answer the question on **G5.1 Resource sheet 8.1**.

TASK 9: More loci

Points to remember

- Loci can be constructed accurately using compasses, a straight edge, a ruler and, if required, a protractor.

- The locus of points that are **a fixed distance from a fixed point** is a circle with centre the fixed point and radius the fixed distance.

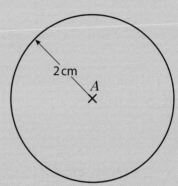

- The locus of points that are **the same distance from a fixed line segment** consists of two parallel lines equidistant from the line segment and two semicircles.

- The locus of points that are **the same distance from two fixed points** is the perpendicular bisector of the line joining the points.

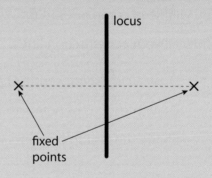

- The locus of points that are **the same distance from two fixed lines** is the bisector of the angle between the two lines.

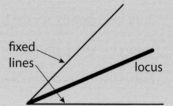

Use plain paper.

You will need compasses, ruler, protractor and sharp pencil.

Show all your construction lines.

① Draw a line 5 cm long.

Construct accurately the locus of points 3 cm from this line.

2 Make an accurate copy of rectangle ABCD.

Draw accurately the set of points that are 3 cm from A.

Draw accurately the set of points that are an equal distance from D and C.

Mark the point that is 3 cm from A and an equal distance from D and C.

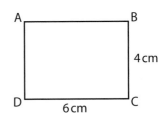

3 The diagram shows a 10 cm by 5 cm rectangle drawn on a centimetre square grid.

The rectangle contains a number of arcs and lines.

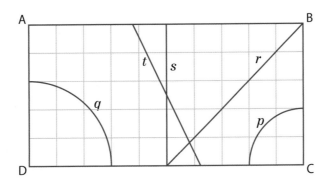

This table describes each arc or line.

Line or arc	Locus
p	Points inside rectangle ABCD exactly 2 cm from C
q	
r	
s	
t	

Copy and complete the table.

Equations, formulae and graphs

TASK 1: Factorising

 Points to remember

⊙ Look for common factors in an algebraic expression and take them outside a bracket.

⊙ Factors can be whole numbers, fractions, decimals or irrational numbers.

⊙ It is good practice to factorise an algebraic expression when presenting answers.

① Multiply out these brackets.

   a $9(3x + 5)$ **b** $8(7x + 6)$

   c $7(4x - 9)$ **d** $3(7x - 12)$

   e $10(2x - 8)$ **f** $6(3x + 5)$

   g $7(7x + 3)$ **h** $5(11x + 25)$

② Factorise these expressions.

   a $21x + 33$ **b** $28t + 36$

   c $60a + 75$ **d** $34y - 40$

   e $42b - 57$ **f** $30w + 42$

   g $24z + 88$ **h** $26d - 65$

③ **a** Write a formula for the perimeter P of the triangle.

   b Factorise the formula.

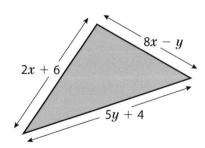

TASK 2: Working with algebraic fractions

 Points to remember

- You can only add or subtract fractions with the same denominator.
- With different denominators, first change the fractions to the same denominator.

In a magic square the sum of the expressions in each row, column and diagonal is the same.

Copy and complete these magic squares.

①

$\dfrac{8}{a}$		$\dfrac{5}{a}$
	$\dfrac{10}{a}$	
		$\dfrac{6}{a}$

②

$\dfrac{12}{b}$	$\dfrac{8}{b}$	
	$\dfrac{9}{b}$	
	$\dfrac{10}{b}$	

TASK 3: Working with formulae

 Points to remember

- When you rearrange formulae, do the same thing to both sides.
- You can use formulae to help solve problems.

① a Make c the subject of $a = bc$

 b Make l the subject of $A = lw$

 c Make L the subject of $M = \dfrac{L}{T}$

 d Make P the subject of $G = \dfrac{K}{P}$

 e Make y the subject of $x = y + az$

 f Make z the subject of $x = y + az$

 g Make h the subject of $V = Ah$

 h Make b the subject of $A = \frac{1}{2}bh$

② a The volume of a hexagonal prism is 330 cm³.
 The area of the cross-section is 22 cm².
 How long is the prism?

 b The area of a circle is 200.96 cm².
 What is the length of its radius? (Use $\pi = 3.14$)

TASK 4: Forming equations

1. The sum of the numbers along the red line is equal to the sum of the numbers along the blue line.

   a Write an expression in x for the sum of the numbers along the red line.

   b Write an expression in x for the sum of the numbers along the blue line.

   c Write an equation in x.

   d Solve the equation for x.

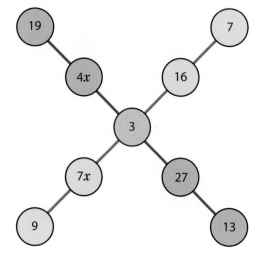

2. The number in each square is found by adding together the numbers in the two adjacent circles.

   a Write the number in A as an expression in x.

   b Write the number in B as an expression in x.

   c Write an equation in x.

   d Solve the equation for x.

   e What are the numbers in A and B?

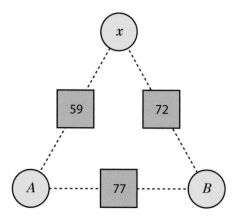

TASK 5: Visualising graphs

 Points to remember

⊙ The normal form of a **linear equation** is $y = ax + b$.
The graph of $y = ax + b$ is a straight line.
a gives the **gradient** of the line and b the **intercept** on the y-axis.

⊙ The graph of a **quadratic equation** $y = ax^2 + b$ is a U-shaped curve.
a changes the gradient of the curve and b moves the curve up or down.

You will need squared paper. For each graph that you sketch, draw a new set of axes.

1. Sketch the graphs of these equations.

   a $y = x + 5$

   c $y = 3x + 7$

   b $y = 2x - 1$

   d $y = 5x - 1$

2. Sketch the graphs of these equations.

   a $y = -x + 3$

   c $y = -2x + 3$

   b $y = -x + 7$

   d $y = -3x$

3. Sketch the graphs of these equations.

   a $y = x^2$

   d $y = x^2 + 9$

   b $y = x^2 + 5$

   e $y = x^2 - 6$

4. Sketch the graphs of these equations.

   a $y = -x^2$

   c $y = -x^2 + 6$

   b $y = -x^2 + 3$

   d $y = -x^2 - 4$

TASK 6: Interpreting graphs

 Points to remember

⊙ Before you interpret a graph, inspect the axes and work out the scales.

⊙ One graph can represent a number of different stories provided that the mathematical facts are correct.

1 This is a graph of Sarah's walk.

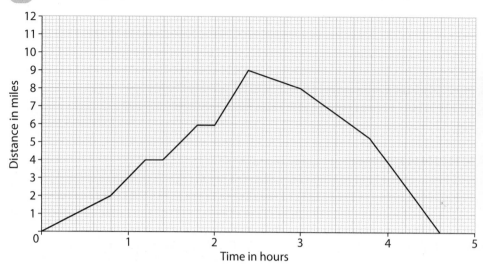

a Sarah left home at 08:30.
   At what time did she arrive at her first stop?

b How far had Sarah walked when she first stopped?

c How long was Sarah's first rest stop?

d How far from home did Sarah walk?

e How long did it take Sarah to walk home?

f Write a short story about Sarah and her day out walking.
   Make sure that you use the correct mathematical information from the graph.

TASK 7: Matching graphs to real-life situations

Points to remember

⊙ Look at what happens as the x-values increase by equal amounts.

⊙ Decide on the relationship between x and y before you try to fit a graph to a real-life situation.

1 Sketch graphs to match these stories.

a A car travels at constant speed.

b A car moves off slowly and gradually gets faster until it reaches a constant speed.

c Water drips at a constant rate into a cylinder.

d A train is moving at constant speed when it applies its brakes and gradually slows down.

e Louise is training by alternately walking at a constant speed for ten metres then running at a constant speed for ten metres.

TASK 8: Using graphs to solve problems

⊙ Points to remember

- For an equation in the form $y = ax + b$:
  - a is the gradient of its graph;
  - $(0, b)$ is the intercept on the y-axis.
- When you know two facts about two unknowns, you can form two equations.
- You can solve two linear equations by finding out where the graphs of the two equations cross.

1   The mass of a jar of jam is x grams.
The mass of a loaf of bread is y grams.

Write expressions for the mass of these combinations.

   a   3 jars of jam and 7 loaves of bread

   b   8 jars of jam and 10 loaves of bread

   c   24 jars of jam and 50 loaves of bread

2   The cost of a bagel is x pence.
The cost of a coffee is y pence.

Write expressions for the total cost of each pair of orders. Simplify the expressions.

   a   One order of 3 bagels and 4 coffees and another of 6 bagels and 5 coffees

   b   One order of 7 bagels and 9 coffees and another of 10 bagels and 4 coffees

   c   One order of 2 bagels and 2 coffees and another of 7 bagels and 12 coffees

3   A cup holds x ml.
A mug holds y ml.

Write expressions for the total number of millilitres for each combination. Simplify the expressions.

   a   4 cups and 6 mugs and 3 cups and 7 mugs

   b   10 cups and 5 mugs and 14 cups and 6 mugs

Probability 2

TASK 1: Theoretical and experimental probability

◉ Points to remember

- For equally likely outcomes, the **theoretical probability** of an event is:

$$\frac{\text{number of favourable outcomes}}{\text{total number of possible outcomes}}$$

- When two events occur at the same time, or one after the other, you can use a list or table to show the equally likely outcomes.

- The **experimental probability** of an event is:

$$\frac{\text{number of successful trials}}{\text{total number of trials}}$$

- You usually get different outcomes when an experiment is repeated.

- As you do more and more trials, the experimental probability becomes closer in value to the theoretical probability.

1. A coin is tossed and a 1 to 6 dice is rolled.
   a Make a list of all the possible outcomes.
   b Make a table of all the possible outcomes.

2. Three teenage boys, Mark, Sam and Daniel, each like a different one of the sports football, tennis or cricket.

   Make a table of all the possibilities of who likes which sport.

3. Five girls, Anna, Billie, Charlie, Daisy and Ella, go to the cinema.

   Billie wants to sit next to Anna.
   Ella wants to sit in an end seat.

   Make a list of all the possible seating arrangements.

TASK 2: Mutually exclusive events

① A fair 1 to 6 dice is rolled once.

Look at this list of events.

    A Rolling a 1

    B Rolling a 2

    C Rolling an odd number

    D Rolling a prime number

a Three pairs of events are mutually exclusive.
List each pair. Explain each of your answers.

b Three pairs of events are **not** mutually exclusive.
List each pair. Explain each of your answers.

② A bag contains some coloured counters. A counter is picked at random.

The probabilities of picking different colours are shown in the table.

Colour	Red	Blue	Green	White
Probability	0.1	0.25	0.3	0.35

a Explain how you know that only red, blue, green or white counters are in the bag.

b Work out the probability of picking:

    i a red or blue counter   **ii** a red, blue or white counter

    iii a yellow counter   **iv** a counter that is not white.

TASK 3: Using experimental probability

> ### Points to remember
> - The **experimental probability** of an event is:
> $$\frac{\text{number of successful trials}}{\text{total number of trials}}$$
> - A bigger number of trials gives a better estimate of probability.
> - When experiments are repeated, there are often different results.

1 Jenny and Peter each carry out an experiment based on this trial.

Drop a 5p coin onto a 20 mm square grid from a height of 10 cm.
Record how many grid lines the 5p coin crosses or touches.

Jenny's results are shown in this table.

Number of grid lines	0	1	2	3	4
Frequency	1	10	11	0	28

Peter's results are shown in this table.

Number of grid lines	0	1	2	3	4
Frequency	0	22	33	0	95

a Work out the experimental probabilities
  i using Jenny's results
  ii using Peter's results
  iii using Jenny's and Peter's results combined.

b Do the experiments give the same results?
  Explain your answer.

c Which set of results gives the most reliable estimate of probability?
  Explain your answer.

d Jenny plans to use the experiment as a fund-raising game at the school fair.

  She suggests that contestants have to pay 5p a turn and can win these prizes.

Number of grid lines	0	1	2	4
Prize	£1	10p	20p	No prize

  Use the experimental results to show that Jenny's suggestion is likely to result in a loss.

TASK 4: Choice or chance?

You will need a set of cards cut out from **S5.4 Resource sheet 4.1** (one car and three goats).

1 The 'Monty Hall Game' is played with four doors.

   There is a car behind one door and a goat behind each of the other three doors.

   The contestants try to win the car by picking the correct door.

   The contestant first chooses a door, without opening it.

   Monty, who knows where the car is, opens two of the other doors to reveal a goat behind each of them.

   The contestant now has a choice, to stick with their initial choice of door, or to change to the other unopened door.

   a What strategy gives the contestant the best chance of winning the car: sticking or changing?

      Explain your answer.

   b Find a friend or an adult to be Monty and to set the cards out for you to simulate the game.

      Play enough times to confirm your answer to part **a**.

Solving problems

TASK 1: History of our number system and zero

 Points to remember

- The Internet is a useful source of information about mathematics and its history.
- You may need to narrow down a search so that it results in (a) less information, and (b) more relevant information.
- It is important to find the right website.
- Menus and a list of options on a website have the same purpose as a list of contents and an index in a book.

Brahmagupta

i Did you know that...?

Mathematicians from many countries helped to develop our number system.

Here are the names of some of them:

Brahmagupta	Pythagoras
Al-Khwarizmi	Cardano
Fibonacci	Al-Uqlidisi
Xu Yue	Ch'in Chiu-Shao
Zhu Shijie	

1. Use the notes you have made during your research on one of the mathematicians.

   You may have been looking at this website:

   www-gap.dcs.st-and.ac.uk/~history/

   Write a short article of two or three paragraphs on the life and work of your mathematician.
   Assume that your article will be published in a magazine for Key Stage 3 pupils.
   Make sure that you give your article a suitable title.

TASK 2: Number puzzles based on 3 by 3 grids

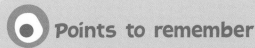

> ## Points to remember
>
> ⊙ Decide which information could be useful.
>
> ⊙ Look for patterns and relationships.
>
> ⊙ Use reasoning to establish what might be possible in the context of the problem and to help you to explain and justify your solution.

You will need a set of 1–9 digit cards. For example, you could use playing cards or you could make nine squares of paper and write 1 to 9 on them.

① Use all the digits 1 to 9.
Use them to make a 'non-magic' square.

Arrange the digits in a 3 by 3 square so that no two rows, columns or corner-to-corner diagonals add up to the same total.

Find two different ways to do it.
Record both ways in your book.

② Use all the digits 1 to 9.
Arrange them in a 3 by 3 square.

Now add each adjacent pair in each row.
This gives you six totals.

For example, for the square on the right the six totals are:

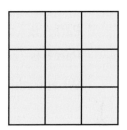

7 + 3 = 10 and 3 + 5 = 8 in the top row

6 + 4 = 10 and 4 + 2 = 6 in the middle row

1 + 9 = 10 and 9 + 8 = 17 in the bottom row.

Now add each of the six totals to form a grand total T.

For this square the grand total T is **10 + 8 + 10 + 6 + 10 + 17 = 61.**

Investigate.
What is the largest possible grand total T?

TASK 3: Exploring fractions

⊙ Points to remember

- ⊙ You can use fractions to describe and compare the areas of shapes.
- ⊙ Showing how calculations with fractions are worked out can help to explain and justify solutions to problems.

You can solve these problems by using fractions.
Explain and justify your answers by showing the calculations that you do with fractions.

(1) This square is divided into three parts.

Part A is $\frac{1}{3}$ of the area of the square.

Part B is $\frac{2}{5}$ of the area of the square.

What fraction of the area of the square is part C?

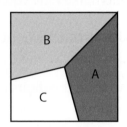

(2) The shapes in the diagram have been formed by joining midpoints of sides.

What fraction of the whole shape is each lettered shape?

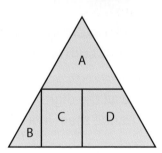

(3) A jug of lemonade is three fifths full.

After one glass of lemonade has been poured out, the jug is half full.

What fraction of a full bottle of lemonade will be left after two more glasses of lemonade have been poured out?

TASK 4: Problems involving properties of numbers

Points to remember

⊙ Breaking a problem into parts can help you to find a suitable starting point for solving it.

⊙ Support your solutions to problems with clear, written explanations and, when appropriate, diagrams.

⊙ You can also use examples to support your explanations.

Solve each problem. Explain clearly how you found your solution.

(1) I am an even multiple of 3.
I am greater than 5^2 and less than 7^2.
The product of my two digits is a cube.
Who am I?

(2) I am a one-digit number.
I differ from my square by a multiple of 3.
The sum of the digits in my cube is neither 9 nor 10.
Who am I?

(3) I am greater than 6^3 and less than 600.
The sum of my digits is 6, the product of my digits is 6 and I am divisible by 6.
Who am I?

(4) $9 = 3^2$ and $16 = 4^2$ are consecutive square numbers.

You can write 85 as the sum of consecutive square numbers because:

$$85 = 36 + 49 = 6^2 + 7^2$$

a Write 365 as the sum of two consecutive square numbers.

b Write 365 as the sum of three consecutive square numbers.

c Is it possible to write 366 as the sum of four consecutive square numbers?

> **Hint**
> You may find it helpful to make a table of square numbers from 1^2 to 12^2.

TASK 5: Using algebra and counter-examples

Example

The sum of three consecutive numbers is 69. What are the numbers?

Let the smallest number be n.
Then the next two numbers are $n + 1$ and $n + 2$.

So $n + (n + 1) + (n + 2) = 69$
$$3n + 3 = 69$$
$$3n = 69 - 3 = 66$$
$$n = 22$$

So the numbers are 22, 23 and 24.

Check $22 + 23 + 24 = 69$

① One number is 5 more than another.
Their sum is 29.
What are the two numbers?

② Jo takes twice as long to walk from her house to the shops as she does to walk back.
The whole journey, not counting her time at the shops, takes her 18 minutes.
How long does Jo take to walk back from the shops?

③ Daniel and Jade have £48 between them.
Daniel has £14 more than Jade.
How much money does Daniel have?

4 David's tennis coach is 42 years older than David.
He is also four times as old as David.
How old is David's tennis coach?

5 Three tickets for Wimbledon cost £76.
The second cost £10 more than the first, and the third £4 less than the second.
How much did each ticket cost?

6 n stands for any positive integer.

Evangeline says that $n^2 + n$ is never a multiple of 8.
Find an example to show that Evangeline is wrong.

Revision unit 1

TASK 1: Using a calculator

 Points to remember

- Estimate the answer to a calculation before you use a calculator.
  Check your calculator answer against your estimate.
- Add brackets, if needed, before you enter calculations in a calculator.
- Make sure that you can use your calculator keys for fractions, powers and roots, brackets and the memory.
- Make sure that you know how to deal with remainders on a calculator.
- Include units in answers to problems where necessary.

1 Write the approximate answer for each of these. Show your working.

a 3.8^3

b $\sqrt{897}$

c $\sqrt{(3.9)^3}$

d $(0.29)^3$

e 0.051×0.48

f $88.7 \div 0.28$

g $\dfrac{4.96 - 1.71}{2.8 + 1.9}$

h $\left(\dfrac{11.75 \div 3.85}{1.1 \times 1.9}\right)^3$

i $\sqrt{\dfrac{49.6 \times 8.06}{0.9}}$

j 29% of £50

k 9.5% of £812

l 74% of £1165

2 **Use your calculator** to work out the answer for each calculation in question **1**.
  Where appropriate, give the answer to a suitable number of decimal places.

TASK 2: Using percentages to compare proportions

 Points to remember

- A proportion is a fraction or percentage.
- When you use percentages to compare proportions in two sets of data, take account of the whole total in each data set.
- When you solve problems, write down the calculation that you will do.
- Check that an answer is reasonable and that it fits the question.

1. The shapes in the diagrams below are divided into equal parts.

   What percentage of the whole shape is each shaded area?

   Give your answer to one decimal place where appropriate.

   a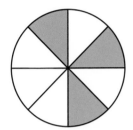

   b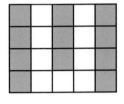

   c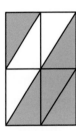

   d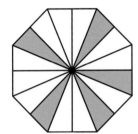

   e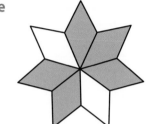

   f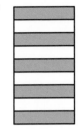

2. The bars show the football matches won, lost and drawn by two teams.

   United has played 30 games. City has played 40 games.

   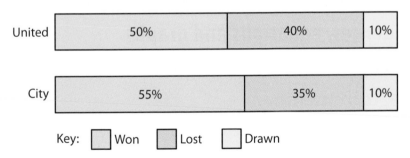

   a Which team has won more games?

   b Which team has lost more games?

   c Which team has drawn more games?

3. Which is more?
   a 49% of £50 or 48% of £51
   b 30% of 60 kg or 32% of 55 kg
   c 25% of £19 or 24% of £20
   d 72% of 65 litres or 65% of 72 litres

2006 level 6

Kate asked people if they read a daily newspaper.
Then she wrote this table to show her results.

No	80 people = 40%
Yes	126 people = 60%

The values in the table **cannot** all be correct.
The error could be in the number of people.

Copy and complete each table to show what the correct numbers could be.

No	80 people = 40%
Yes	………… people = 60%

No	………… people = 40%
Yes	126 people = 60%

TASK 3: Sequences, equations and graphs

⊙ Points to remember

- ⊙ The difference between consecutive terms of a linear sequence can help you to find the nth term.
- ⊙ In algebra, letters represent numbers.
- ⊙ When you solve an equation, what you do to one side you must do to the other side.
- ⊙ For a graph, the x-axis is the line $y = 0$ and the y-axis is the line $x = 0$.

① *2001 level 6*

Look at these equations.

$$3a + 6b = 24 \qquad 2c - d = 3$$

a Use the equations to work out the value of the expressions below.

   i $8c - 4d$ ii $a + 2b$ iii $d - 2c$

b Use one or both of the equations to write an expression that has a value of 21.

2 *1997 level 6*

Here is a sequence of shapes made from squares.

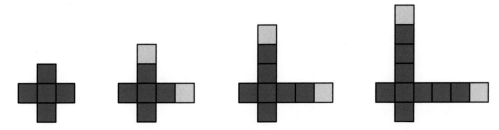

Shape number (n)	1	2	3	4
Number of squares (s)	5	7	9	11

A formula connects the number of squares (s) used in a shape, with the shape number (n).

Which one of these formulae is it?

$$s = 3n + 2 \qquad s = 3n + 1 \qquad s = 2n + 3 \qquad s = 5n - 3 \qquad s = 2n + 5$$

3 *2001 level 6*

Solve these equations. Show your working.

a $7 + 5k = 8k + 1$

b $10y + 23 = 4y + 26$

4 *2001 level 6*

Here is the graph of $y = x - 7$.

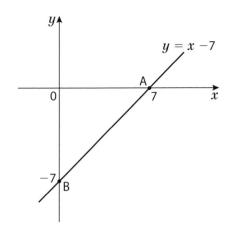

Write the coordinates of one point on the line between A and B.

TASK 4: Angles and polygons

⊙ Points to remember

- ⊙ Angles on a straight line sum to 180°.
- ⊙ Angles at a point sum to 360°.
- ⊙ The angle sum of a triangle is 180°.
- ⊙ Angles in a quadrilateral sum to 360°.
- ⊙ The angle sum of an n-sided polygon is $180 \times (n - 2)$ degrees.
- ⊙ The exterior angles of any polygon sum to 360°.

Example

The exterior angle of a regular polygon is 60°.

a How many sides has the polygon?

The exterior angles of any polygon sum to 360°.

So the polygon has $360° \div 60° = 6$ angles and hence 6 sides.

b What is the angle sum of the polygon?

The angle sum of a polygon with n sides is $180 \times (n - 2)$ degrees.

Since the polygon has 6 sides, substitute $n = 6$.

The angle sum of the polygon is $180° \times (6 - 2) = 180° \times 4 = 720°$.

---

① One angle in the diagram on the right is given as 95°.

Copy the diagram.

Write the size in degrees of each of the other angles.

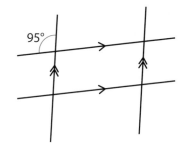

② One angle of a parallelogram is 64°.

What are the other three angles?

③ Angle ACE is 48°.

Angle BDE is 63°.

Calculate the size of angle DBE.

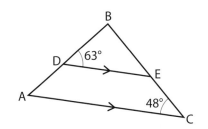

④ a Calculate the sum of the interior angles of a regular 20-sided polygon.

b Calculate the size of one exterior angle of a regular 20-sided polygon.

⑤ The exterior angle of a regular polygon is 24°.

a How many sides has the regular polygon?

b What is the size of an interior angle?

c What is the angle sum of the interior angles?

TASK 5: Charts and diagrams

◉ Points to remember

⊙ In a **pie chart**:
  – the angle at the centre of the circle is proportional to the frequency for that category;
  – the number of degrees for one item is 360° ÷ total number of items.

⊙ A **stem-and-leaf diagram** shows data in order from lowest to highest. You can use it to work out the mode, median and range.

⑤ *2001 level 6*

A teacher asked two different classes:
'What type of book is your favourite?'

a Here are the results from class A (total 20 pupils).

Draw a pie chart to show this information.

Show your working and draw your angles accurately.

Type of book	Frequency
Crime	3
Non-fiction	13
Fantasy	4

b The pie chart shows the results from all of class B. Each pupil had only one vote.

The sector for non-fiction represents 11 pupils.

How many pupils are in class B?
Show your working.

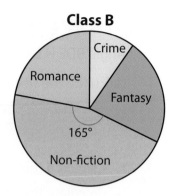

Class B

② *2002 level 6*

Three types of mice might come into our homes.

Some mice are more likely to be found in homes far from woodland.
Others are more likely to be found in homes close to woodland.

The bar charts show the percentages of mice that are of each type.

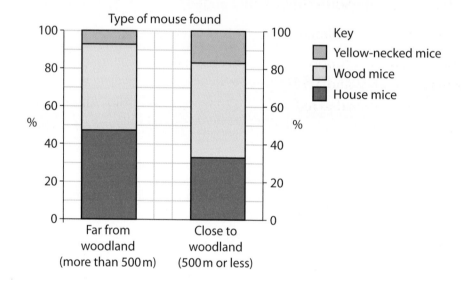

a About what percentage of mice in homes close to woodland are wood mice?

b About what percentage of mice in homes far from woodland are not wood mice?

c The red bars show the percentages for house mice.
One of the red bars is taller than the other.

Does that mean there must be more house mice in homes far from woodland than in homes close to woodland? Explain your answer.

Revision unit 2

TASK 1: Ratio and proportion

Points to remember

- A ratio compares two quantities in the same units,
  e.g. 50p : £1 is 1 : 2, 200 : 50 = 4 : 1.

- Two sets of numbers are **directly proportional** if the ratio of corresponding pairs is always the same.

- Pairs of numbers that are directly proportional lie on a straight-line graph.

- When you solve direct proportion problems you can:
  - use equivalent ratios and a scaling method;
  - use the unitary method to reduce the value of one of the variables to 1.

Example 1

The ratio of boys to girls in a class is 3 : 5. There are 12 boys.

How many girls are there?

Since $3 + 5 = 8$, the boys are $\frac{3}{8}$ and the girls are $\frac{5}{8}$ of the class.

Since $\frac{3}{8}$ is 12 pupils, $\frac{1}{8}$ is $12 \div 3 = 4$ pupils, and $\frac{5}{8}$ is $4 \times 5 = 20$ pupils.

Example 2

It takes me 1.5 minutes to swim 2 lengths of the pool.

How many lengths can I swim in 15 minutes?

Unitary method

	Time (min)	Number of lengths
	1.5	2
÷ 1.5	1	$2 \div 1.5$
× 15	15	$2 \div 1.5 \times 15 = 20$

Answer: I can swim 20 lengths in 15 minutes.

1 *2003 level 6*

Paul is 14 years old. His sister is exactly 6 years younger, so this year she is 8 years old.

This year, the ratio of Paul's age to his sister's age is 14 : 8
14 : 8 written as simply as possible is 7 : 4

a When Paul is 21, what will be the ratio of Paul's age to his sister's age?
Write the ratio as simply as possible.

b When his sister is 36, what will be the ratio of Paul's age to his sister's age?
Write the ratio as simply as possible.

c Could the ratio of their ages ever be 7 : 7?
Write **Yes** or **No**. Explain how you know.

2 *2001 level 6*

Two parts of this square design are
shaded yellow.

Two parts are shaded grey.

Show that the ratio of yellow to grey is 5 : 3.

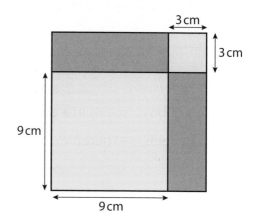

3 a In a survey, people were asked:
‘What kind of lunch did you have today?’
The pie chart shows the results.
15 people said ‘No lunch’.
How many people said ‘Hot lunch’?
Show your working.

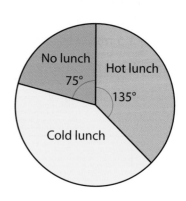

b In a different survey, 120 people were asked about their favourite TV programmes.

45 people said 'Game shows'.

On a pie chart, what would the angle be for the sector 'Game shows'? Show your working.

TASK 2: Solving number problems

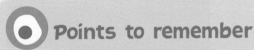
Points to remember

When you are solving problems:

⊙ read the problem and identify key information;

⊙ write down the calculation that you need to do;

⊙ choose a suitable calculation method and, if you use a written method, show your working;

⊙ check your answer for accuracy and make sure that it fits the question.

1 *2003 level 6*

The information in the box describes three different squares, A, B and C.

Put squares A, B and C in order of size, starting with the smallest.

| The area of square A is 36 cm². |
| The side length of square B is 36 cm. |
| The perimeter of square C is 36 cm. |

Show calculations to explain how you work out your answer.

2 *2004 level 6*

Copy and complete the table by writing in the missing numbers.
The first row is done for you.

First number	Second number	Sum of first and second numbers	Product of first and second numbers
3	6	9	18
5	−3		
−8		−5	

3 *2000 level 6*

A garden centre sells plants for hedges.

The table shows what the centre sold in one week.

Plants	Number of plants sold	Takings
Beech	125	£212.50
Leylandii	650	£2437.50
Privet	35	£45.50
Hawthorn	18	£23.40
Laurel	5	£32.25
Total	833	£2751.15

a What percentage of the total number of plants sold was leylandii? Show your working.

b What percentage of the total takings was for leylandii? Show your working.

c Which is the cheaper plant, beech or privet? Show working to explain how you know.

4 *2001 level 6*

This sequence of five numbers follows the rule 'subtract 10, then divide by 10'.

Copy and complete the sequence.

　　　□　　120　　11　　0.1　　□

TASK 3: Expressions, equations and formulae

◉ Points to remember

- ⊙ When you use algebra to solve problems, first decide what letters you are going to use and then set up an equation or formula.
- ⊙ When a formula is written as $y = \ldots$, y is the subject of the formula.
- ⊙ You can rearrange a formula to make another letter the subject.
- ⊙ When you rearrange a formula or equation, you must do the same thing to both sides.

You can substitute numbers into a formula like this:

Example

To change temperature measured in degrees Fahrenheit to degrees Celsius you can use this formula: $C = \frac{5}{9}(F - 32)$.

Suppose the temperature is 77 degrees Fahrenheit.

Then substitute $F = 77$ to get:

$C = \frac{5}{9}(77 - 32) = \frac{5}{9} \times 45 = 25$

So 77 degrees Fahrenheit is equivalent to 25 degrees Celsius.

1 *2001 level 5*

A cookery book shows how long, in minutes, it takes to cook a joint of meat.

> **Microwave oven**
>
> Time = (12 × weight in pounds) + 15

> **Electric oven**
>
> Time = (30 × weight in pounds) + 35

a How long will it take to cook a 3 pound joint of meat in a microwave oven?

b How long will it take to cook a 7 pound joint of meat in an electric oven?

c How much quicker is it to cook a 2 pound joint of meat in a microwave oven than in an electric oven?

2 *2001 level 6*

You can work out the cost of an advert in a newspaper by using this formula:

$C = 15n + 75$

C is the cost in pounds.
n is the number of words in the advert.

a An advert has 18 words.

Work out the cost of the advert.
Show your working.

b The cost of an advert is £615.

How many words are in the advert?
Show your working.

2004 level 6

Doctors sometimes use this formula to calculate how much medicine to give a child.

$$c = \frac{ay}{12 + y}$$

c is the correct amount for a child, in ml

a is the amount for an adult, in ml

y is the age of the child, in years

A child who is 4 years old needs some medicine. The amount for an adult is 20 ml.

Use the formula to work out the correct amount for this child.
You must show your working.

TASK 4: Circles and enlargements

⦿ Points to remember

⊙ This triangle can help you to work out the circumference (C)
or diameter (d) of a circle.

⊙ The area of a circle = $\pi \times$ (radius)^2.

⊙ When a shape is enlarged:
  – each length is multiplied by the scale factor
  – the area is multiplied by (scale factor)^2
  – angles remain the same.

Example 1

Calculate the area of a circle with a diameter of 48 inches.
Write your answer to the nearest whole number.

Radius = diameter ÷ 2

Radius = 48 ÷ 2 = 24 inches

Area of circle = $\pi \times$ (radius)^2 = $\pi \times$ (24)^2 = 1809.557... = 1810 square inches

Example 2

A 1 cm cube is enlarged by a scale factor of 2.
What is the volume of the enlarged cube?

The new dimensions are 2 cm by 2 cm by 2 cm.

The volume is 2 × 2 × 2 = 8 cm^3

① A circle has a radius of 5.4 cm.

   a What is the length of the circumference to one decimal place?

   b What is the area of the circle to one decimal place?

② The diameter of a circle is 47.9 m.

   Calculate the area of the circle to the nearest whole number.

③ A semicircle has a radius of 7 mm.

   Calculate the area of the semicircle to one decimal place.

④ The diagram shows two rectangles.
   The big rectangle is an enlargement of the small rectangle.

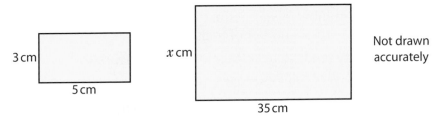

Not drawn accurately

   a Find the missing length x cm.

   b How many of the smaller rectangles will fit into the larger rectangle without overlapping?

⑤ A cuboid has dimensions 1 mm by 7 mm by 8 mm.

   The lengths are all enlarged by a scale factor of 3.

   What is the volume of the enlarged cuboid?

⑥ The distance between Ulverston and Coniston in Cumbria is 22.4 km.

   A map has a scale of 1 cm for every 4 km.

   What is the distance between Ulverston and Coniston on the map?

Coniston Water, Cumbria

TASK 5: Probability

① *1995 level 6*

Alun has these two spinners.

Alun spins both spinners and then adds the numbers to get a total.

He starts to make a list of all the possible totals.

a Complete Alun's list. Start like this.

Totals
———
5

b Alun says: 'There are 9 possible totals altogether.

So the probability of getting a total of 5 is $\frac{1}{9}$.'

Explain why Alun is wrong.

c The actual probability that Alun gets a total of 5 is $\frac{1}{16}$.

What is the probability of not getting a total of 5?

2 *2005 level 6*

Here is some information about all the pupils in class 9A.

	girls	boys
right-handed	13	14
left-handed	1	2

A teacher is going to choose a pupil from 9A at random.

a What is the probability that the pupil chosen will be a girl?

b What is the probability that the pupil chosen will be left-handed?

c The teacher chooses the pupil at random.
She tells the class the pupil is left-handed.

What is the probability that this left-handed pupil is a boy?

3 *2000 level 6*

I have two bags of counters.

Bag A contains 12 red counters and 18 yellow counters.

Bag B contains 10 red counters and 16 yellow counters.

I am going to take one counter at random from either bag A or bag B.

I want to get a red counter.
Which bag should I choose?

Show working to explain your answer.